D0335978

Key Stage Three
Maths
The Practice Tests

As you get towards the end of Key Stage 3, your school is likely to set you some tests to find out how you're doing in Maths.

Happily, this CGP book contains three complete sets of Maths practice tests so that you can go into the real thing fully prepared. We've even included detailed answers so that you can mark your own work.

What CGP is all about

Our sole aim here at CGP is to produce the highest quality books — carefully written, immaculately presented and dangerously close to being funny.

Then we work our socks off to get them out to you — at the cheapest possible prices.

Published by CGP

Editors:
David Maliphant, Matteo Orsini Jones.

Contributors:
Cath Brown, Jane Chow, Kieran Wardell.

With thanks to Hayley Thompson for the proofreading.
With thanks to Laura Jakubowski for the copyright research.

ISBN: 978 1 84762 255 6

Clipart from Corel®
Printed by Elanders Ltd, Newcastle upon Tyne

Contents

How to Use This Book

This book contains loads of practice papers for Key Stage 3 Maths.

Understandably you're desperate to get started, but just hold your horses — there are **a few things you should know** first:

Here's What This Book Contains...

There are **three** sets of papers.

There are **answers** for all the questions and **mark schemes** at the back of the book. Use these to mark your work **after** you've had a go at the papers.

This is what's included in **each set** of papers:

Paper	Time Allowed	Marks Available
Paper A (no calculator)	1 hour	60
Paper B (calculator)	1 hour	60

To Get the Best Marks You Need to Keep Practising

1) These practice papers won't make you better at Maths, but they will show you what you **can** do, and what you **can't do**.

2) Do a test, **mark it** and look at what you got **wrong**. **That's** the stuff you need to **work on**.

3) **Go away**, **learn** those tricky bits, then **do the <u>same</u> test again**. If you're **still** getting questions wrong, you'll have to do even **more practice** and **test yourself again**. Keep going until you get the **best possible marks**.

4) It doesn't sound like a lot of **fun**, but it really will **help**.

Seven Top Tips for Doing Well

1) **Read everything properly**

   The most important thing is to **understand** the questions. Read everything **carefully** to be sure you're doing what they want.

2) **Follow all the instructions**

   Some questions have special instructions.

   For example, this pencil ✎ means "**WRITE YOUR ANSWER HERE**". So make sure you do.

3) **Look at the marks available**

   The **number of marks** you can get for a question gives you an idea of **how long** you should spend on that question — spend **more time** on questions worth **more marks**.

4) **Write your answers as clearly as you can**

   In a real exam, whoever's marking your paper won't be able to give you a mark if they can't read your answer — even if it's right.

5) **Show your working**

Make sure you write down your working whenever you do a calculation.
Even if you get the answer **wrong**, you could get a mark for trying to do the
question in the **right way**. Questions which award marks for working have
a pencil marking the space where you should **clearly show your working**.

6) **Check your work**

Don't throw away easy marks — even if a question looks dead simple,
you have to check your answer and make sure it's sensible.

7) **Use spare paper**

If you're going to do the practice papers more than once,
write your answers on a separate bit of paper.

Recording Your Progress

You can use the table below to keep a **record** of **how well you do** in each test.
Don't forget to **look back** at what you got **wrong**, so you know what to **practise**
for the **next test**.

Stick Your Marks in Here:

		Paper A (out of 60)	Paper B (out of 60)	Total Score (out of 120)
Set 1	First go	5 3		
	Second go			
	Third go			
Set 2	First go			
	Second go			
	Third go			
Set 3	First go			
	Second go			
	Third go			

Levels

As of **September 2014**, there are no KS3 assessment levels. But you can use the table
below to see what grades you'd have been likely to get under the **old levelling system**.

You'll need to use your **total score** for one paper set.

Mark	120-105	104-64	63-42	41-30	under 30
Level	**8**	**7**	**6**	**5**	**N**

Key Stage 3

Mathematics Test

Practice Paper 1A
Calculator NOT allowed

Read this page, but don't open the booklet until your teacher says you can start. Write your name and school in the spaces below.

First Name _____

Last Name _____

School _____

Remember

■ The test is one hour long.

■ Make sure you have these things with you before you start:
pen, pencil, rubber, ruler, angle measurer or protractor
and pair of compasses.
You may use tracing paper.

■ There are some formulas you might need on the next page.

■ The easier questions are at the start of the test.

■ Try to answer all of the questions.

■ Don't use any rough paper — write all your answers and working in this test paper.

■ Check your work carefully before the end of the test.

■ If you're not sure what to do, ask your teacher.

Instructions

 This means write down your answer or show your working and your answer.

 You may not use a calculator in this test.

Formulas

Trapezium

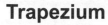
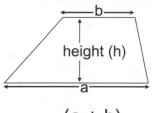

Area = $\dfrac{(a + b)}{2} \times h$

Prism

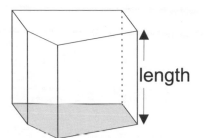

length

Volume = area of cross-section × length

---

1. ABCD is a rhombus. Angle A is 53°.

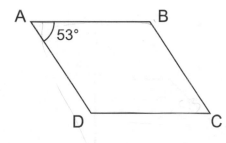

(DIAGRAM NOT TO SCALE)

(a) Write down the size of angle C.

 C = ...53...... °

 1 mark

(b) Work out the size of angle B.

 B = ...127...... °

 2 marks

---

2. Complete the following statements.

(a) 700 cm³ = ...700...... millilitres = ...0.7...... litres

(b) 63000 grams = ...63...... kilograms = ...0.063...... tonnes

3. Enlarge the shape below by a scale factor of ½, about centre of enlargement (0,0).

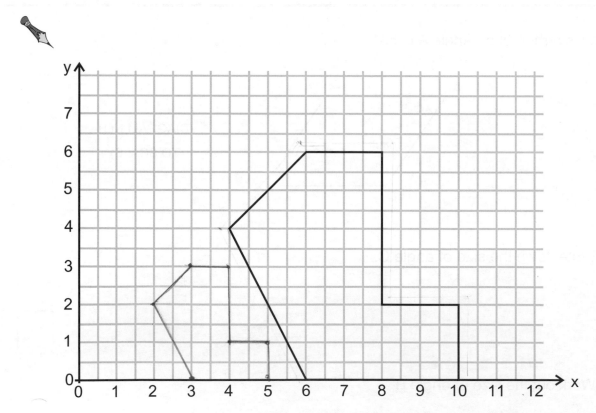

4. 120 Year 9 students were being taken on a school trip.
    They could choose between a day at a theme park or the seaside.

    41 boys wanted to go to the theme park.

    14 girls wanted to go to the seaside.

    56 of the students were girls.

    Complete the table to show where the students decided to go.

	Theme Park	Seaside	Total
Boys	41	23	64
Girls	42	14	56
Total	83	37	120

2 marks

5. Gazza and Julia have each cut a rectangle out of paper.

One side is 10 cm.
The other side is n cm.

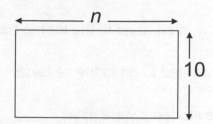

(a) They write down expressions for the perimeter of the rectangle.

Julia writes $2n + 20$

Gazza writes $2(n + 10)$

Put a circle around the correct statement below.

Julia is correct and Gazza is wrong.

Julia is wrong and Gazza is correct.

Both Julia and Gazza are correct.

Both Julia and Gazza are wrong.

1 mark

(b) Gazza cuts his rectangle in half.
He puts the halves side by side.

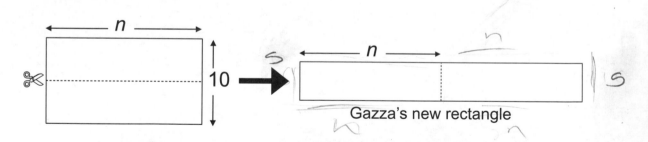

Gazza's new rectangle

What is the perimeter of Gazza's new rectangle?
Write your expression out as simply as possible.

    $n+n+n+n+ 5+5$ $4n+10$

$4n+10$

.............................$4n+10$.............................

2 marks

Continued over the page

(c) Julia cuts her rectangle in half a different way.
     She puts them together to form a new rectangle.

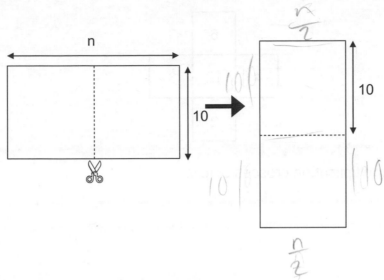

What is the perimeter of Julia's new rectangle?
Write your expression as simply as possible.

$$10 + 10 + 10 + 10 + \frac{n}{2} + \frac{n}{2}$$

$$n + 40$$

........................$n + 40$........................

2 marks

(d) What value of n would make the perimeter of Julia's
     new rectangle the same value as the perimeter of
     Gazza's new rectangle?

$$n + 40 = 4n + 10$$
$$n + 30 = 4n$$
$$30 = 3n$$
$$10 = n$$

........................$n = 10$........................

1 mark

6. The diagram below shows a multiplication cross.

Opposite squares multiply together to give the answer in the middle square.

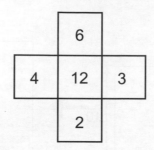

Complete the multiplication crosses below.

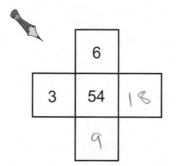

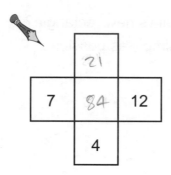

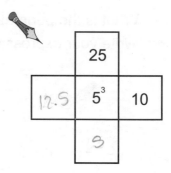

4 marks

7. Eleanor pays 14p per minute for a phone call to Morocco.

The total cost of the phone call is £8.96.

Work out the length of the call in minutes.

14
28
42
56
70
84

$$\begin{array}{r} 0\,6\,4 \\ 14\overline{)896} \\ 84\downarrow \\ \overline{056} \\ 56 \\ \overline{0} \end{array}$$

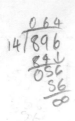 ......64...... minutes

2 marks

8. Solve these equations:

(a) $\dfrac{3x}{9} = -2$

$3x = -18$

$x = -6$

x = ...–6........

1 mark

(b) $2y - 6 = 24$ $+6$

$2y = 30$

$y = 15$

y = ...15.........

1 mark

(c) $3z - 7 = 29 + z$

$3z = 36 + z$

$2z = 36$

$z = 18$

z = ...18.........

2 marks

9. A survey was conducted to find out how many people were registered with a National Health Service dentist, a private dentist or no dentist.

The pie chart shows the results.

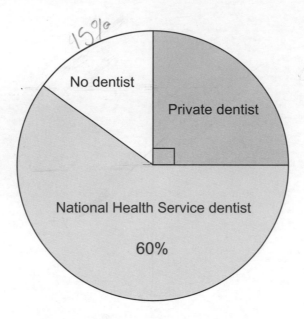

15%

No dentist

Private dentist

National Health Service dentist

60%

(a) The angle on the pie chart for the people registered with a private dentist is 90°. What percentage of the people is this?

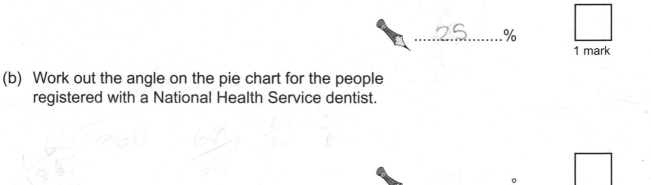

.........25.........%

1 mark

(b) Work out the angle on the pie chart for the people registered with a National Health Service dentist.

..................°

2 marks

(c) 300 people were not registered with a dentist.

Work out how many people took part in the survey.

....

2 marks

10. Look at these fractions:

$$\frac{3}{4} \qquad \frac{1}{2} \qquad \frac{5}{8}$$

(a) Work out the range of the fractions.

$$\frac{6}{8} - \frac{4}{8} = \frac{2}{8}$$

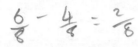

.... $\frac{2}{8}$ ....

☐ 1 mark

(b) Work out the mean of the fractions.

$$\frac{6}{8} + \frac{4}{8} + \frac{5}{8} = \frac{15}{8}$$

$$\frac{15}{8} \div 3 \quad \frac{5}{8}$$

.... $\frac{5}{8}$ ....

☐ 2 marks

11. On a school trip the ratio of teachers to pupils was 2 : 7.
108 people went on the trip.

How many teachers and how many pupils went on the trip?

 ....24....... teachers and ....84...... pupils

☐ 3 marks

$$2 + 7 = 9$$

$$108 \div 9 = 12$$

$$12 \times 2 = 24$$

$$12 \times 8 = \frac{84}{108}$$

Maths — Practice Paper 1A

12. In the year 2020, Josie will be x years old.

Her mum will be exactly four times Josie's age.

Josie's Nanna is 30 years older than her Mum.

Josie's Nanna will be 78 years old in 2020.

(a) Use this information to form an algebraic expression and solve it to find x. You must show your working.

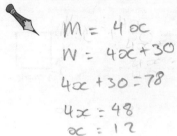

$$M = 4x$$
$$N = 4x + 30$$
$$4x + 30 = 78$$
$$4x = 48$$
$$x = 12$$

x = ...12..........

2 marks

(b) In what year was Josie born?

.....2008.....

1 mark

13. Here is the graph of the straight line $y = -2x + 3$.

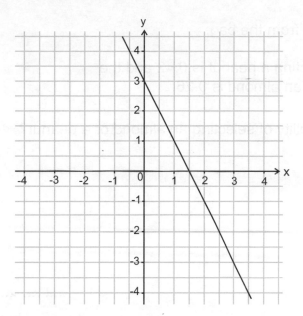

(a) A point on the line $y = -2x + 3$ has an x-coordinate of 25.

What is the y-coordinate of the point?

$-2x + 3$

$-2 \times 25 + 3$

$-50 + 3$

-53

 ....−47........

1 mark

(b) A point on the line $y = -2x + 3$ has a y-coordinate of -31.

What is the x-coordinate of the point?

$-31 = -2x + 3$

$-28 = -2x$

$14 = x$

....−14........

1 mark

(c) Using an algebraic method, find the point that lies on both
the straight lines $y = -2x + 3$ and $y = 6x - 17$.

You must show your working.

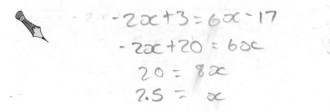

$-2x + 3 = 6x - 17$

$-2x + 20 = 6x$

$20 = 8x$

$2.5 = x$

$-2x + 3$

$-2 \times 2.5 + 3$

$-5 + 3$

-2

(..2.5. , ..−2....)

3 marks

14. A bag of 50 mixed nuts contains almonds, peanuts and cashew nuts.

I randomly select a nut from the bag.

The probability of selecting a peanut is 0.42 and the probability of selecting an almond is 0.26.

(a) What is the probability of selecting an almond or a peanut?

.........0.68............ ☐
1 mark

(b) What is the probability of selecting a cashew nut?

.........0.32............ ☐
1 mark

(c) How many peanuts are in the bag?

.........21............ ☐
1 mark

15. In a school 75% of the pupils have fillings.

20% of the pupils with fillings also have braces.

Work out the percentage of pupils in the school with fillings and braces.

$$75\% \times 20\%$$
$$75\% \times \frac{1}{5}$$

.............15.........%

3 marks

16. (a) Rearrange the equation $2d + 6 = e$ to make d the subject.

$$2d + 6 = e$$
$$2d = e - 6$$
$$d = \frac{e - 6}{2}$$

$d = \dfrac{e-6}{2}$

1 mark

(b) Rearrange the equation $8 + 5f^2 = 3g$ to make f the subject.

$$8 + 5f^2 = 3g$$
$$5f^2 = 3g - 8$$
$$f^2 = \frac{3g - 8}{5}$$
$$f = \sqrt{\frac{3g - 8}{5}}$$

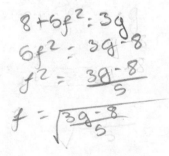

$f = \sqrt{\dfrac{3g-8}{5}}$

2 marks

Maths — Practice Paper 1A

17. You have these numbers:

0.1	3	20	0.2	0.03	1

(a) Choose the two numbers which give the lowest answer.
Fill in the blanks and work out the answer.

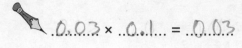 $0.03 \times 0.1 = 0.03$

2 marks

(b) Which two numbers give the answer 200?

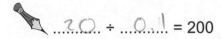 $20 \div 0.1 = 200$

1 mark

(c) Look at these expressions.

$$p - 3 \qquad 2p \qquad p^2 \qquad \frac{2}{p} \qquad \frac{p}{2}$$

Which gives the greatest value when p is between 0 and 1?

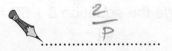 $\frac{2}{p}$

1 mark

18. These two kites are similar:

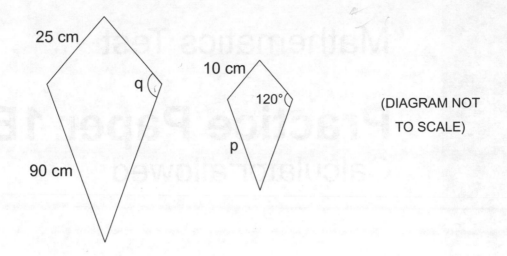

25 cm

q

10 cm

120°

p

90 cm

(DIAGRAM NOT TO SCALE)

(a) Work out the length of side p in the smaller kite.

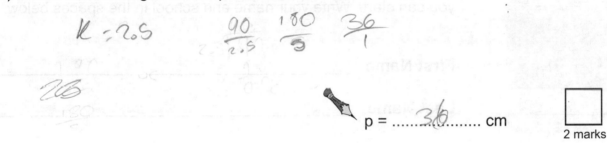

$k = 2.5$ $\dfrac{90}{2.5}$ $\dfrac{180}{5}$ $\dfrac{36}{1}$

26

p = ...36...... cm

2 marks

(b) What is the size of angle q in the larger kite?

q = ...120...... °

1 mark

END OF TEST

Key Stage 3

Mathematics Test

Practice Paper 1B

Calculator allowed

Read this page, but don't open the booklet until your teacher says you can start. Write your name and school in the spaces below.

First Name _____

Last Name _____

School _____

Remember

■ The test is one hour long.

■ Make sure you have these things with you before you start: pen, pencil, rubber, ruler, calculator, angle measurer or protractor and pair of compasses.
You may use tracing paper.

■ There are some formulas you might need on the next page.

■ The easier questions are at the start of the test.

■ Try to answer all of the questions.

■ Don't use any rough paper — write all your answers and working in this test paper.

■ Check your work carefully before the end of the test.

■ If you're not sure what to do, ask your teacher.

Instructions

This means write down your answer or show your working and your answer.

You may use a calculator in this test.

Formulas

Trapezium

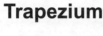

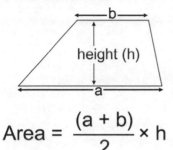

Area = $\dfrac{(a + b)}{2} \times h$

Prism

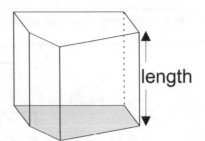

length

Volume = area of cross-section × length

---

1. (a) Use your calculator to find the answer to $\sqrt{15200} \div 3.2^4$.
Write down the full answer displayed on your calculator.

....

1 mark

(b) Round your answer to part (a) to three decimal places.

....

1 mark

(c) Use your calculator to find the answer to

$$\frac{151 - 39}{90 - 55} = \text{...................}$$

1 mark

2. (a) Shade in four tenths of this shape:

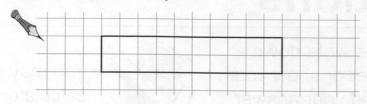

1 mark

(b) What proportion of this shape is shaded?
Give your answer as a decimal number.

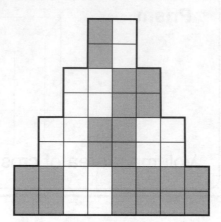

.... 1 mark

(c) What percentage of this diagram is shaded?

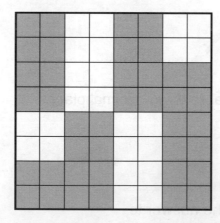

.... % 1 mark

3. (a) This diagram has four small squares shaded in.

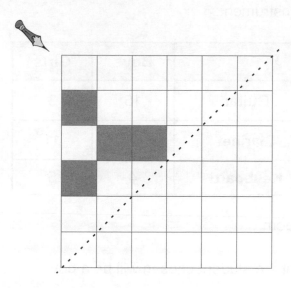

Shade in four more small squares to make a pattern that has a line of symmetry along the dotted line.

2 marks

(b) Here is another diagram with four small squares shaded in.

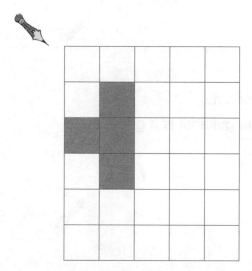

Shade in four more small squares to make a pattern that has rotational symmetry of order two.

2 marks

4. This table shows the number of students in a school who are learning to play a musical instrument:

	Boys	Girls
Guitar	15	3
Clarinet	2	11
Keyboard	4	5

A student is chosen at random.

(a) Find the probability that the student chosen will be a boy.

.... ☐
1 mark

(b) Find the probability that the student chosen will play the keyboard.

.... ☐
1 mark

(c) A guitarist is chosen at random.
Find the probability that the guitarist is a girl.

.... ☐
1 mark

5. Shops A and B both sell cans of cola.

Cola only 36p per can

Shop A

SPECIAL DEAL
Pack of 6 cans of Cola

only £2.19

Shop B

(a) How much does it cost to buy 8 cans of Cola from shop A?

£ ....

(b) Abigail wants to buy 18 cans of Cola.
Which shop would be cheaper and by how much?
You must show your working.

Shop .... by £ ....

6. Mr Smith is on a diet. He weighs 105 kg. His target weight is 77 kg.

If he loses 1.4 kg each week, how many weeks will it take him to reach his target weight?

.... weeks

7. Simplify these expressions:

(a) $6 - 3s + 5s - 2$

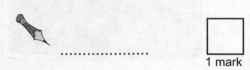 .... □ 1 mark

(b) $9t^2 + 3t + 2t^2$

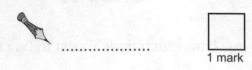 .... □ 1 mark

(c) $6u \times 3u$

.... □ 1 mark

(d) $\dfrac{16v^3}{4v}$

.... □ 1 mark

8. The table shows the speed in miles per hour of a tennis player's serve during a match.

Speed (s) in mph	frequency (f)	midpoint (x)	fx
90 < s ≤ 100	12	95	1140
100 < s ≤ 110	18	....	....
110 < s ≤ 120	28	....	....
120 < s ≤ 130	7	....	....
Total	65	-	7125

(a) Complete the table.

2 marks

(b) Work out an estimate of the mean speed of the tennis player's serve.

 .... mph

1 mark

9. The diagram shows the trapezium ABCD.

Angle A measures 130° and angles B and C are both right angles.

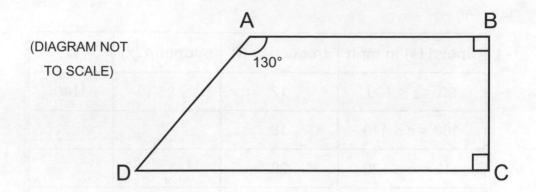

The trapezium is cut into two shapes labelled P and Q.

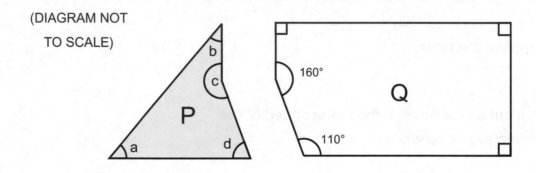

Work out the sizes of angles a, b, c and d.

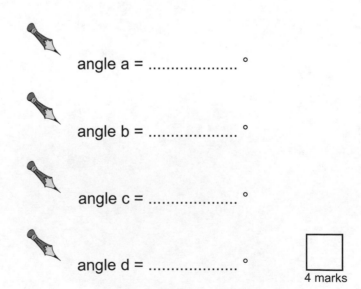

angle a = ... °

angle b = ... °

angle c = ... °

angle d = ... °

4 marks

10. In a sale, the price of a digital camera is reduced by 18%.
The new price of the camera is £287.

(a) Work out the price of the camera before the sale.

£...................

2 marks

(b) Jenny takes 120 photographs with her digital camera.
She prints off 54 photographs and discards the rest.

Work out the percentage of the photographs that are discarded.

.... %

2 marks

11. A glass tumbler is a cylinder with a radius of 3 cm and a height of 12 cm.

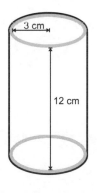

(DIAGRAM NOT
TO SCALE)

Calculate the volume of the glass tumbler.

.... cm³

2 marks

12.

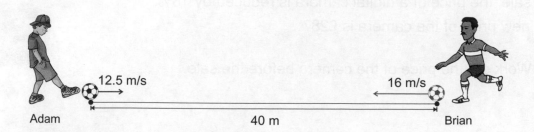

12.5 m/s

16 m/s

Adam

40 m

Brian

Adam and Brian are standing 40 metres apart.

Adam kicks a ball to Brian at an average speed of 12.5 m/s.

Brian kicks the ball back to Adam at an average speed of 16 m/s.

Work out the total time, in seconds, that the ball takes to travel from Adam to Brian and back again.

.... seconds

2 marks

13. In one week, Andy delivered 114 newspapers.

He delivered the same number of newspapers on Monday, Tuesday and Wednesday.

On Thursday he delivered half the number of papers he had delivered on Monday.

He delivered 10 newspapers each day on Friday, Saturday and Sunday.

How many newspapers did he deliver on Tuesday?

....

☐ 3 marks

14. Multiply out the brackets in this expression.
Write your answer as simply as possible.

(x + 7)(x − 4)

....

☐ 2 marks

15. The points P and Q lie on a straight-line graph, as shown below.

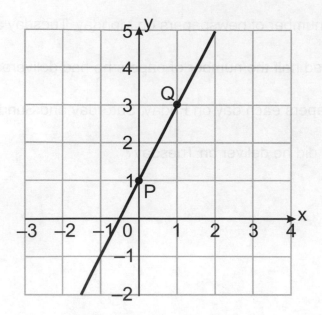

(a) Write down the coordinates of P and Q.

 P is (............ , ...) and Q is (............ , ...)

1 mark

(b) Show that the gradient of the line PQ is 2.

2 marks

(c) Write down the equation of the line that points P and Q lie on.

 ....

1 mark

16. Body mass index is a number used to identify possible weight problems in adults. The table below shows how it can be interpreted.

Body mass index (b)	Weight Status
$b < 18.5$	Underweight
$18.5 \leq b < 25$	Normal
$25 \leq b < 30$	Overweight
$b \geq 30$	Obese

A person's body mass index is calculated using the formula

$$b = \frac{w}{h^2}$$

where **b** = body mass index, **w** = weight in kg and **h** = height in metres.

(a) Adam weighs 70 kilograms and is 1.75 metres tall.
Work out his body mass index and find his weight status.

Body mass index = ...   Weight status = ...

 2 marks

(b) Jodie has a body mass index of 19 and weighs 55 kilograms.
Work out how tall she is. Give your answer correct to 2 decimal places.

.... m

 2 marks

(c) Daniel is 1.64 metres tall and has a body mass index of 28.
How much weight must he lose to achieve a body mass index of 24?
Give your answer to the nearest kilogram.

.... kg

 3 marks

Maths — Practice Paper 1B

17. The diagram shows the cross-section of a dry ski slope.

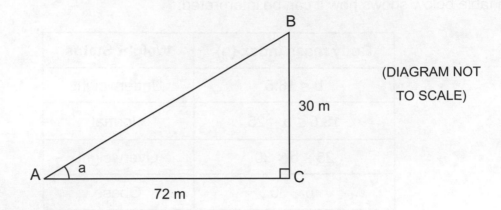

(DIAGRAM NOT TO SCALE)

The ski slope AB stands on horizontal ground AC of length 72 m.
The height of the ski slope is 30 m.

(a) Work out the length of the ski slope AB.

.... m

2 marks

(b) The ski slope makes an angle of a° with the horizontal.
Work out the size of angle a. Give your answer correct to 1 decimal place.

.... °

2 marks

18. On any given day in June, the probability that the pollen count will be high is 0.6.

(a) What is the probability that the pollen count will not be high?

....

(b) On how many days would you expect the pollen count not to be high in June?

....

(c) Find the probability that the pollen count will be high on each of the first three days in June.

....

END OF TEST

Key Stage 3

Mathematics Test

Practice Paper 2A
Calculator NOT allowed

Read this page, but don't open the booklet until your teacher says you can start. Write your name and school in the spaces below.

First Name _____

Last Name _____

School _____

Remember

■ The test is one hour long.

■ Make sure you have these things with you before you start: pen, pencil, rubber, ruler, angle measurer or protractor and pair of compasses.
You may use tracing paper.

■ There are some formulas you might need on the next page.

■ The easier questions are at the start of the test.

■ Try to answer all of the questions.

■ Don't use any rough paper — write all your answers and working in this test paper.

■ Check your work carefully before the end of the test.

■ If you're not sure what to do, ask your teacher.

Instructions

This means write down your answer or show your working and your answer.

You may not use a calculator in this test.

Formulas

Trapezium

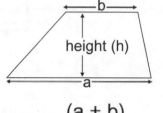

Area = $\dfrac{(a + b)}{2} \times h$

Prism

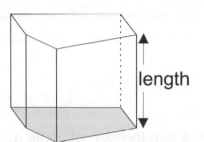

Volume = area of cross-section × length

---

1. A bag of fruit sweets contains 5 strawberry flavour,
4 raspberry flavour and 6 blackberry flavour.

Debbie chooses a sweet at random. Find the probability that it is:

(a) raspberry flavour

 ....

1 mark

(b) not blackberry flavour

 ....

1 mark

(c) Steve has another bag of fruit sweets. Half of them are strawberry flavour.
Tick the correct box to show who has the most strawberry sweets.

☐ Debbie   ☐ Steve   ☐ Cannot tell

Explain your answer.

1 mark

2. (a) Construct this triangle accurately in the space below.

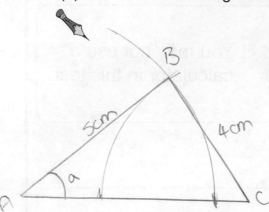

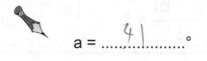

(DIAGRAM NOT TO SCALE)

5 cm

4 cm

6 cm

A B C a

3 marks

(b) Measure the size of angle a.

a = ...41.........°

1 mark

3. Mr. Wardell ordered 52 calculators for the Maths department.
Each calculator cost £2.32.

Estimate how much Mr. Wardell spent on calculators.

£....................

2 marks

4. The diagram shows how to work out the cost of hiring a cement mixer and having it delivered.

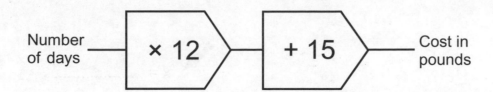

$$\text{Number of days} \quad \boxed{\times 12} \quad \boxed{+ 15} \quad \text{Cost in pounds}$$

(a) How much would it cost to hire the cement mixer for 7 days?

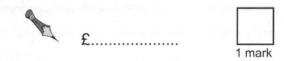

£....................

1 mark

(b) Marlon paid £147.
How many days did he have the cement mixer for?

....

2 marks

(c) The 12 in the diagram above represents the daily charge for hiring the cement mixer.

What does the 15 represent?

....

1 mark

5. Solve the following equations:

(a) $3x + 7 = 25$

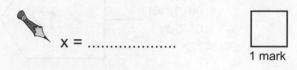

x = ...

1 mark

(b) $4(x - 2) = 30$

x = ...

1 mark

(c) $2x - 9 = 5x + 3$

x = ...

1 mark

6. Fill in the gaps to complete these calculations correctly:

(a) $7 +$ .... $= 2$

1 mark

(b) $5 -$ .... $= 8$

1 mark

(c) $-2 \times$ .... $= -8$

1 mark

(d) .... $\div -4 = -3$

1 mark

7. The cuboid below is made of 2 cm cubes.

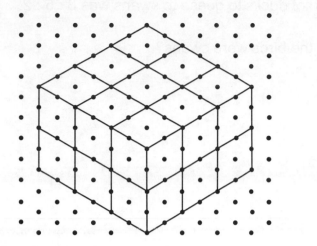

(DIAGRAM NOT
TO SCALE)

(a) What is the volume of the cuboid?

 .... cm³

1 mark

(b) What is the surface area of the cuboid?

.... cm²

2 marks

(c) The diagram shows a 2 cm cube. Add more 2 cm cubes
to form a cuboid with a volume of 48 cm³.

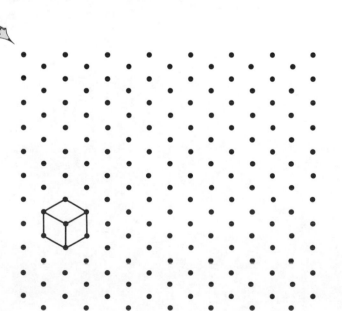

(DIAGRAM NOT
TO SCALE)

2 marks

8. Roop was studying the birds at a wildlife sanctuary.
    She noticed that the ratio of ducks to geese to swans was 3 : 5 : 2.

    (a) What percentage of the birds were swans?

    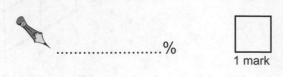
    ....%

    1 mark

    (b) She counted 18 ducks. How many geese and swans were there?

    .... geese

    .... swans

    2 marks

9. Write the following values in order of size, starting with the smallest.

0.3 $\qquad$ ½ $\qquad$ ⅖ $\qquad$ 0.2

....

3 marks

10. Here are six sequences and six expressions.

Match each sequence with the correct expression for its nth term.
The first one has been done for you.

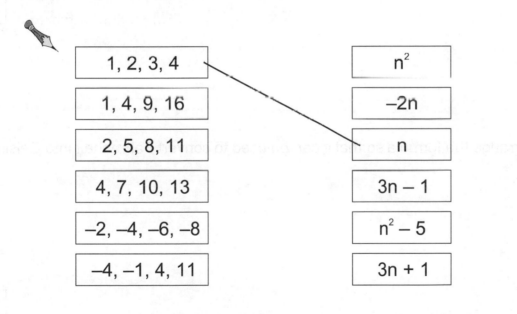

1, 2, 3, 4	n^2
1, 4, 9, 16	$-2n$
2, 5, 8, 11	n
4, 7, 10, 13	$3n - 1$
$-2, -4, -6, -8$	$n^2 - 5$
$-4, -1, 4, 11$	$3n + 1$

2 marks

11. The formula for converting temperature in Celsius (C) to Fahrenheit (F) is

$$F = \frac{9C}{5} + 32$$

(a) Convert 10°C into Fahrenheit.

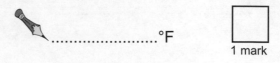 ....°F

☐ 1 mark

(b) Convert -20°C into Fahrenheit.

.....................°F

☐ 2 marks

(c) Rearrange the formula so that it can be used to convert Fahrenheit into Celsius.

C = ...

☐ 2 marks

12. Look at the triangle below.

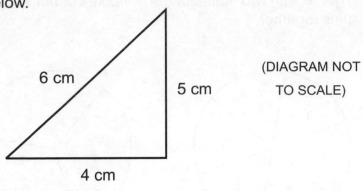

6 cm

5 cm

4 cm

(DIAGRAM NOT TO SCALE)

Is this a right-angled triangle? Explain how you know.

2 marks

13. Expand and simplify the following expression.

$$(x + 5)(x + 4)$$

....

2 marks

14. Pat is playing a game with two spinners. She works out her score by multiplying the two numbers she spins together.

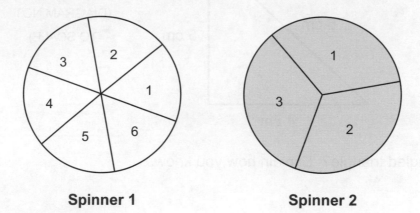

Spinner 1   Spinner 2

(a) Complete the table to show all her possible scores.

Spinner 1

	1	2	3	4	5	6
1	1	2	....	....	....	....
2	2	4	....	....	....	....
3	3	6	....	....	....	....

Spinner 2

2 marks

(b) Use your table to work out the probability that Pat's score is an odd number.

....

1 mark

15. The diagram shows an equilateral triangle ABC.

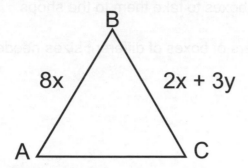

Side AB is of length 8x. Side BC is of length 2x + 3y.
The perimeter of the triangle is 36.

Use algebra to find the values of x and y.

x = ...

y = ...

3 marks

16. A cake machine produces 10 000 cakes at a time.
The cakes have to be put into boxes to take them to the shops.

(a) The table shows the numbers of boxes of different sizes needed
to hold all of these cakes.

Complete the table:

Number of cakes per box	100		500		2000	5000
Number of boxes		40	20	10		2

3 marks

(b) Write an equation using symbols to connect **T**, the number of cakes
made at a time, **B,** the capacity of a box and **N**, the number of boxes.

....

1 mark

(c) The factory gets a new machine which produces cakes
at a rate of 50 per minute.
How long does it now take to produce 10 000 cakes?

Show your working.

.... hours .... minutes

2 marks

17. The highest mountain in the world is Mount Everest.
Its height in feet is 2.903×10^4.

(a) Write 2.903×10^4 as an ordinary number.

.... ☐ 1 mark

(b) The highest mountain in the UK is Ben Nevis.
Its height in feet is 4.41×10^3.

How much higher is Mount Everest than Ben Nevis?
Give your answer in standard form.

.... feet ☐ 2 marks

18. Find the value of y in each of the equations below.

(a) $6^y = 1$

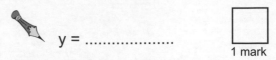

y = ...

1 mark

(b) $3^y = 81$

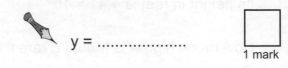

y = ...

1 mark

(c) $72 = y^3 \times 3^2$

y = ...

1 mark

END OF TEST

Key Stage 3

Mathematics Test

Practice Paper 2B
Calculator allowed

Maths

KEY STAGE
3

PRACTICE PAPER
2B

Read this page, but don't open the booklet until your teacher says you can start. Write your name and school in the spaces below.

First Name   *Orla*

Last Name   *Taylor.*

School

Remember

- The test is one hour long.

- Make sure you have these things with you before you start: pen, pencil, rubber, ruler, calculator, angle measurer or protractor and pair of compasses.
  You may use tracing paper.

- There are some formulas you might need on the next page.

- The easier questions are at the start of the test.

- Try to answer all of the questions.

- Don't use any rough paper — write all your answers and working in this test paper.

- Check your work carefully before the end of the test.

- If you're not sure what to do, ask your teacher.

Instructions

This means write down your answer or show your working and your answer.

You may use a calculator in this test.

Formulas

Trapezium

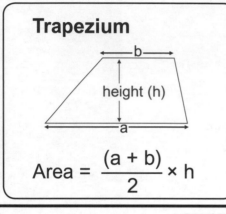

Area = $\dfrac{(a + b)}{2} \times h$

Prism

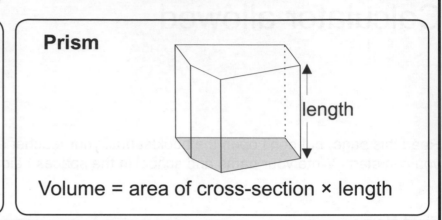

Volume = area of cross-section × length

---

1. The diagram shows two flags and a straight line.

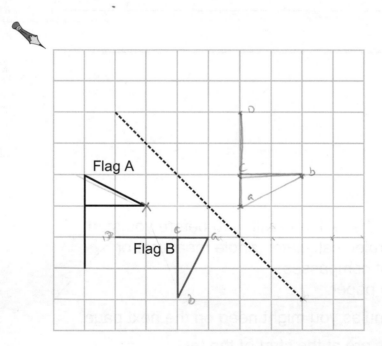

(a) Flag A has been rotated 90° clockwise to give Flag B.
Mark the centre of rotation with a cross.

1 mark

(b) Flag B is reflected in the straight line. Draw its new position.

1 mark

2. Jeff wants to buy a bottle of water from a vending machine.
The bottle costs 45p. Jeff only has 5p, 10p and 20p coins.

Complete the table to show all the ways he can pay exactly 45p.

Number of 5p coins	Number of 10p coins	Number of 20p coins
1	0	2
3	1	1
5	2	0
7	1	0
9	0	0

3 marks

3. (a) Shade $\frac{4}{7}$ of this shape:

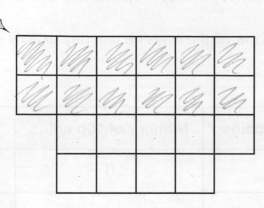

1 mark

(b) Shade 0.3 of this shape:

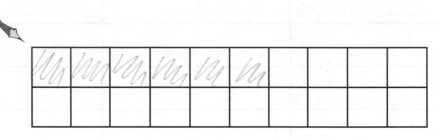

1 mark

(c) Shade 45% of this shape:

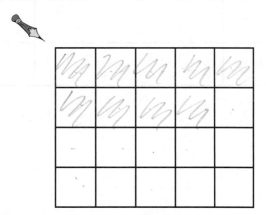

1 mark

4. Peter timed how long it took him to do his last five sets of Maths homework.

Set	Time to do homework (minutes)
1	17
2	26
3	52
4	31
5	43

(a) What is the range of the times taken?

........35...... minutes

1 mark ✓

(b) What was the median time taken?

...3.4.:.2..... minutes

1 mark

(c) Pattie timed how long it took her to do the same five sets of homework.

The range of her times was 20 minutes.
The median of her times was 25 minutes.

Write down a set of times that Pattie might have taken.

Set	Time
1	15
2	20
3	20
4	30
5	40

2 marks

5. Helen drew two pie charts to show what pets are owned by students in classes 9A and 9B.

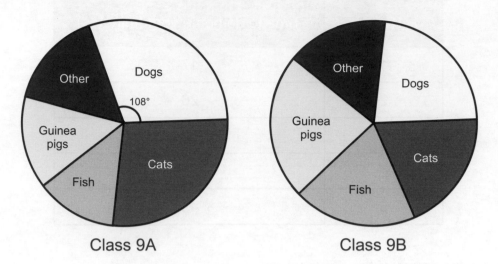

Class 9A   Class 9B

(a) In class 9A, the section for dogs represents 9 students.

How many students are in class 9A?

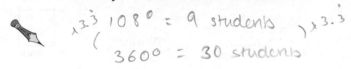

$_{\times 3.3}$ 108° = 9 students $_{\times 3.3}$

(3600° = 30 students

........30........

2 marks

(b) Tick the box to say which class has the most dog owners.

☐ ✓   ☐   ☐

9A   9B   Cannot tell

Explain your answer.

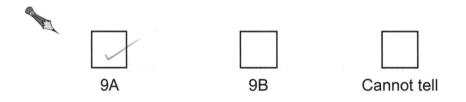

The angle for the no. dog owners ⌐in 9A is obtuse whereas the angle in 9B is acute so it is less.

✓

1 mark

6. (a) Write down three pairs of coordinates that fit the rule **x + y = 7**.

(...2..., ...5...), (...3..., ..4......), (...1..., ...6...)

(b) Draw the graph of x + y = 7 on the grid below.

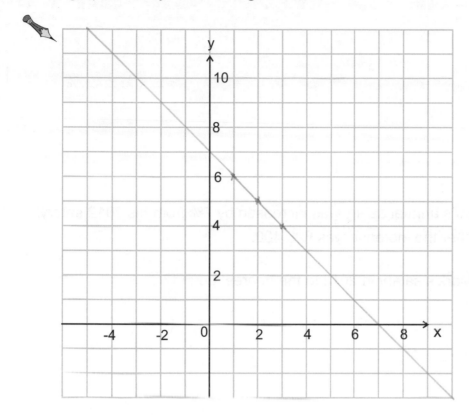

7. The diagram shows part of Bekani's garden.

The crosses represent the positions of two trees.

He wants to lay a path so that it is equidistant from the two trees.

Construct the locus that the path should take.

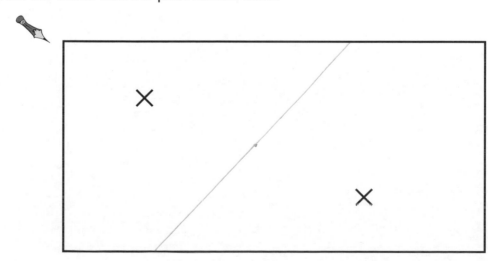

Maths — Practice Paper 2B

57

8. In 2012 Gail's annual salary was £32 200.

In 2013 her salary was increased to £35 800.

(a) What was the percentage increase in her salary?

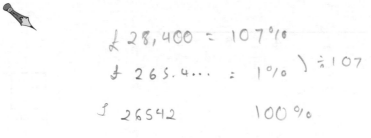

$35,800 - 32,200 = 3600$

$\cdot 100\% = 32,200$

$\div 8.94 ($

$11.2\% = 3600$ $) \div 8.94$

..............11.2.........%

2 marks

(b) In 2013 Mark's annual salary was increased by 7% from his 2012 salary.

His salary after the increase was £28 400.

What was Mark's salary in 2012 to the nearest pound?

$£28,400 = 107\%$

$£265.4... = 1\%$ $) \div 107$

$£26542$ 100%

£.......26542...

2 marks

9. Miss Singleton asked her Year 9 form group how much time they had spent watching television over the weekend.

The answers are shown in the graph below.

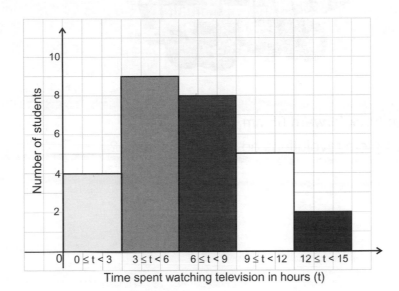

Time spent watching television in hours (t)

(a) How many students did she ask?

 .... 28 ....

1 mark

(b) Calculate an estimate of the mean time spent watching television.
Give your answer in hours and minutes to the nearest 10 minutes.

.... hours and .... minutes

3 marks

10. The wheels on Dominic's toy truck have a diameter of 2 cm.

(a) He pushes the truck forward 65 cm.
    How many complete revolutions do the wheels make?

.... | 2 marks

(b) What is the area of the cross section of a wheel on the truck?

.... cm^2 | 2 marks

The toy is a scale model of a real truck.

The cross sectional area of a wheel on the real truck is 0.58 m².

(c) Find the scale factor of the enlargement that would transform
    the toy truck into a truck the same size as the real truck.

.... | 3 marks

11. The diagram shows part of the edge of a regular polygon.

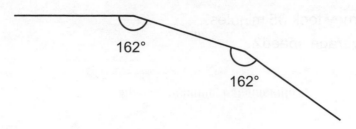

162°

162°

(a) What size are the exterior angles of the polygon?

.... °

1 mark

(b) How many sides does the polygon have?

....

1 mark

12. Louise travels 18 miles to work.

(a) One day the journey took 35 minutes.
What was her average speed?

$35/60 = 0.583$ hrs

$18/0.583 = 30.874785591766...$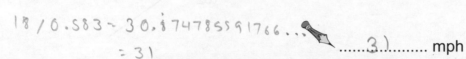

$= 31$

.......3.)......... mph

1 mark ✓

(b) If she drove at an average speed of 38 miles per hour,
how long would it take her to get to work?

$38/18 = 2.1$

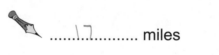 ....12.6........ minutes

1 mark

(c) Clarissa took 25 minutes to drive to work.
Her average speed during the journey was 40 miles per hour.
How long was her journey?

$25/60 = 0.416$

$40 \times 0.416 = 16.66$

 ....1.7........... miles

1 mark

13. Find the missing side x in each of the following right-angled triangles.

(a)

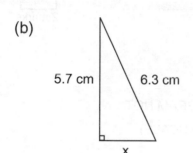
3.4 cm

x

7.3 cm

(DIAGRAM NOT
TO SCALE)

x = ...8...1......... cm

2 marks

(b)

5.7 cm   6.3 cm

x

(DIAGRAM NOT
TO SCALE)

x = ...2..7......... cm

2 marks

14. The formula for the volume, V, of a sphere of radius r is $V = \frac{4}{3}\pi r^3$.

(a) Find the volume of a sphere with radius 3.6 cm.

$4/3 \times \pi \times 3.6^3 \quad = 195.43$

.....195.43... cm³

2 marks

(b) Find the radius of a sphere with a volume of 28.3 cm³.

$28.3 \div (4/3 \times \pi) = 6.756127334$

.....6.8...... cm

2 marks

15. (a) Find the size of angle a in the right-angled triangle below.

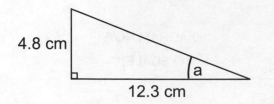

4.8 cm

(DIAGRAM NOT

TO SCALE)

12.3 cm

a

$\tan(a) = \frac{4.8}{12.3}$

a = ...21..32.....°

2 marks

(b) Find the length of side b in this right-angled triangle:

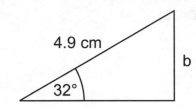

4.9 cm

b

32°

(DIAGRAM NOT

TO SCALE)

$\sin(32) = \frac{b}{4.9}$

$4.9 \sin(32) = b$

$= 2.596604395$

b = ...2.6........ cm

2 marks

16. The Clewes family and the Bleach family visited the Italian Gardens.

The Clewes family consisted of 3 adults and 2 children and they were charged £31.

The Bleach family consisted of 2 adults and 5 children and they were charged £39.

(a) Using **a** to represent the adult cost and **c** to represent the child cost, write down 2 equations.

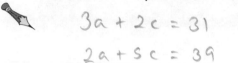

$$3a + 2c = 31$$
$$2a + 5c = 39$$

2 marks

(b) Solve your equations to find the cost of entry for adults and children. You must show an algebraic method.

$$3a + 2c = 31$$
$$2a + 5c = 39 \quad \times -1.5 \quad = -3a - 7.5 = -58.5$$

$$3a + 2c = 31$$
$$-3a - 7.5c = 58.5$$

$$-5.5c = -27.5 \quad \times 2$$

$$-11c = -55 \quad \times -1$$

 a = £ 7

$$11c = 55$$
$$c = 5$$

c = £ 5

2 marks

$$3a + 2c = 31 \qquad 2a + 5c = 39$$
$$3a + 2(5) = 31 \qquad 2(7) + 5(5) = 39$$
$$3a + 10 = 31 \qquad 14 + 25 = 39 ✓$$
$$3a = 21$$
$$a = 7$$

17. The diagram shows three similar rectangles — A, B and C.

×1.6   ×1.75

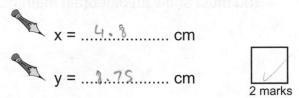

A 3 cm   B 5 cm   C y 8.75

x
4.8

8 cm   14 cm

(DIAGRAM NOT TO SCALE)   ×1.75

÷2.916

(a) Find the missing lengths x and y.

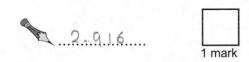

x = ...4.8... cm

y = ...1.75... cm

2 marks ✓

(b) What is the scale factor of the enlargement that
would transform C to A?

...2.916...

1 mark

END OF TEST

Key Stage 3

Mathematics Test

Practice Paper 3A
Calculator NOT allowed

Read this page, but don't open the booklet until your teacher says
you can start. Write your name and school in the spaces below.

First Name _Orla_

Last Name _Taylor_

School

Remember

- The test is one hour long.

- Make sure you have these things with you before you start:
  pen, pencil, rubber, ruler, angle measurer or protractor
  and pair of compasses.
  You may use tracing paper.

- There are some formulas you might need on the next page.

- The easier questions are at the start of the test.

- Try to answer all of the questions.

- Don't use any rough paper — write all your answers and
  working in this test paper.

- Check your work carefully before the end of the test.

- If you're not sure what to do, ask your teacher.

Instructions

This means write down your answer or show your working and your answer.

You may not use a calculator in this test.

Formulas

Trapezium

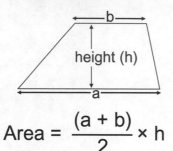

b

height (h)

a

Area = $\dfrac{(a + b)}{2} \times h$

Prism

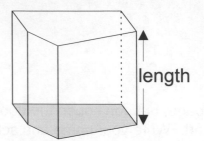

length

Volume = area of cross-section × length

---

1. (a) Show that 8 × 37 = 296.

$$\begin{array}{r} \overset{5}{3}7 \\ \times\ 8 \\ \hline 2\,9\,6 \end{array}$$

1 mark

(b) What is 32 × 37? You can use part (a) to help you.

$$\begin{array}{r} 32 \\ \times\ 37 \\ \hline 2\,1\,4 \\ 9\,6\,0 \\ \hline 1\,1\,7\,4 \end{array}$$

.........1174.........

2 marks

2. David is d years old.
His younger sister Katya is k years old.
Their father is three times as old as David.

Write down expressions for each of the following:

(a) David's age in 10 years time.

_____d + 10_____

1 mark

(b) Katya's age 7 years ago.

_____k − 7_____

1 mark

(c) Their father's age.

_____3d_____

1 mark

(d) The difference between their father's age and David's age.
Simplify your answer as much as possible.

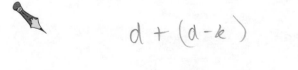
3d = f

_____3d − d_____

1 mark

(e) David's age, when Katya is as old as he is now.
Simplify your answer as much as possible.

$d + (d - k)$

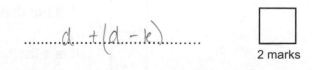
_____d + (d − k)_____

2 marks

3. A triangle has a base 20 cm long.
The area of the triangle is 100 cm².

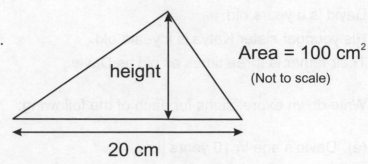

Area = 100 cm²
(Not to scale)

height

20 cm

What is the perpendicular height of the triangle? Show your working.

area = ½ b×h

100 = ½ 20 × h

200 = 20 × h

10 = h

$\frac{10 \times 20}{2}$ $\frac{200}{2}$ = 100 ✓

..............10.......... cm

2 marks

4. (a) I am thinking of a number. My number is a multiple of 3.

Anish says: "Because 3 is an odd number, your number must be odd."

Is Anish correct? Explain your answer.

No, when an odd number is multiplied by
an even number, the answer is always even.
Eg. 3 × 4 = 12   12 is even.

2 marks

(b) I am thinking of a different number. It is a multiple of 12.

Tick all the statements from the list below that must be true.

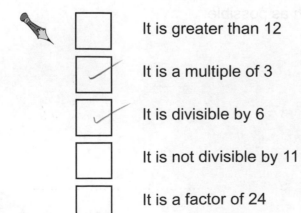

☐ It is greater than 12

☑ It is a multiple of 3

☑ It is divisible by 6

☐ It is not divisible by 11

☐ It is a factor of 24

2 marks

5. Look at this sequence of patterns made with crosses:

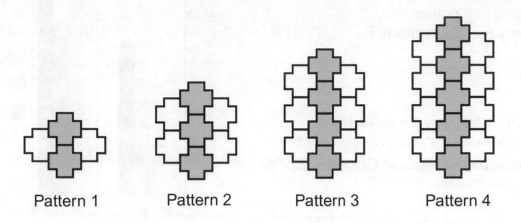

Pattern 1   Pattern 2   Pattern 3   Pattern 4

(a) How many grey crosses will there be in the 10th pattern?

 ....11..........

1 mark

(b) How many white crosses will there be in the 10th pattern?

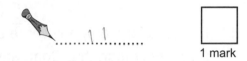 ....20.........

1 mark

(c) How many crosses will there be altogether in the 100th pattern?

 ....1050.........

1 mark

6. Fill in the missing fraction in each of the sums below.

(a) $\dfrac{1}{7} + \dfrac{1}{5} = \dfrac{5}{35} + \dfrac{7}{35} = \dfrac{12}{35}$  ....12/35.........

1 mark

(b) $\dfrac{2}{13} - \dfrac{2}{39} = \dfrac{6}{39} - \dfrac{2}{39} = \dfrac{4}{39}$ ....4/39.........

1 mark

7. The bar graph shows the percentage increase in sales of books by two publishing companies, Company A and Company B.

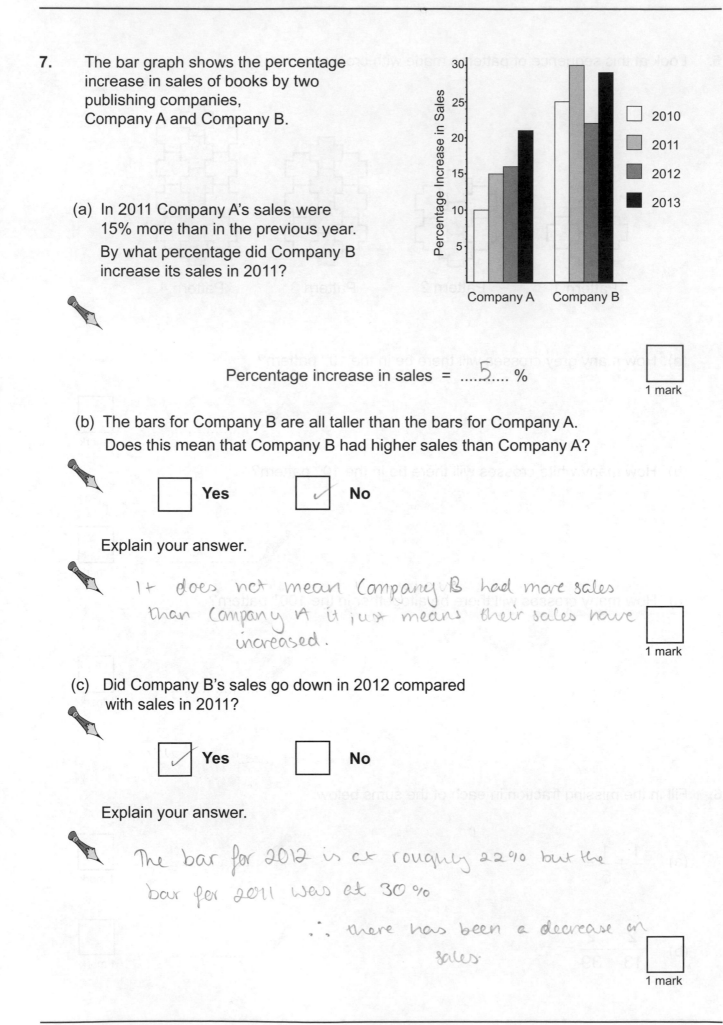

Percentage Increase in Sales

□ 2010
▨ 2011
▨ 2012
■ 2013

Company A   Company B

(a) In 2011 Company A's sales were 15% more than in the previous year.

By what percentage did Company B increase its sales in 2011?

Percentage increase in sales = ...5..... %

1 mark

(b) The bars for Company B are all taller than the bars for Company A.

Does this mean that Company B had higher sales than Company A?

☐ **Yes**   ☑ **No**

Explain your answer.

It does not mean Company B had more sales than Company A it just means their sales have increased.

1 mark

(c) Did Company B's sales go down in 2012 compared with sales in 2011?

☑ **Yes**   ☐ **No**

Explain your answer.

The bar for 2012 is at roughly 22% but the bar for 2011 was at 30%

∴ there has been a decrease on sales.

1 mark

8. The diagram shows two common sizes of paper, called A4 and A3.

A3 paper is an enlargement of A4 paper.

One A3 sheet is exactly the same size as two A4 sheets next to each other.

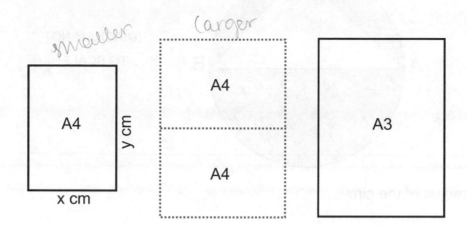

A4 paper is x cm wide and y cm long.

(a) Use the second diagram to write down the width and length of A3 paper.

Width = ...*y*......... cm

Length = ...*2x*...... cm

(b) Explain why $\dfrac{2x}{y} = \dfrac{y}{x}$.

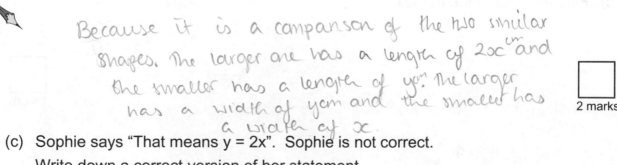

Because it is a comparison of the two similar shapes. The larger one has a length of 2x cm and the smaller has a length of y cm. The larger has a width of y cm and the smaller has a width of x.

(c) Sophie says "That means y = 2x". Sophie is not correct.

Write down a correct version of her statement.

y = ...

9. The diagram shows a circle with diameter AB, which contains the triangle ABC. The circle has an area of 4π cm².

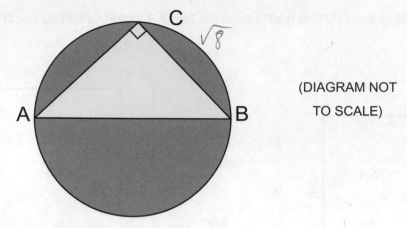

C

$\sqrt{8}$

A   B

(DIAGRAM NOT TO SCALE)

(a) Find the radius of the circle.

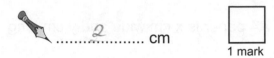 ....2............ cm

1 mark

(b) The side BC of the right-angled triangle is $\sqrt{8}$ cm.
Show that the triangle is isosceles.

2 marks

(c) Find the area of the triangle.

$$\cos 90° = \frac{\sqrt{8}}{AB}$$

$$AB = \frac{\sqrt{8}}{\cos 90°}$$

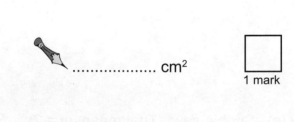 .... cm²

1 mark

10. At a party there are:

25 three-year olds

20 four-year olds

two mothers, aged 28 and 32

three fathers, aged 30, 31 and 33

one grandmother, aged 68

(a) Put the following in order, from smallest to largest.
(You do not need to do any calculations.)

| **mean age** | **median age** | **modal age** |

1. ......median......................

2. ......modal......................

3. ......mean......................

1 mark

(b) Explain how you knew which was the largest without working it out.

The median does not take into account the other ages

1 mark

11. In my Gran's cupboard, she has tins of peaches, pineapple and pears.
The tins are either large or small.
The table shows the numbers of each type of tin Gran has.

	Large tins	Small tins	
Peaches	4	3	7
Pineapple	8	4	12
Pears	2	3	5
	14	10	

(a) Gran chooses a tin at random.
What is the probability it is a small tin of pears?

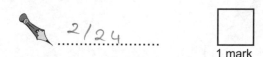

2/24

1 mark

(b) My younger sister takes the labels off all of the tins.
Gran wants a tin of peaches.

Which size tin should Gran open to have the best chance of getting a
tin of peaches? Explain your answer, including any calculations.

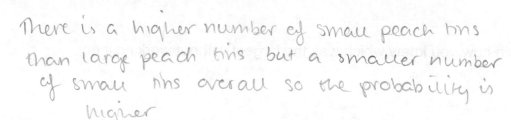

There is a higher number of small peach tins
than large peach tins but a smaller number
of small tins overall so the probability is
higher

small tin of peaches = 3/10
Large tin of peaches = 2/14

3 marks

∴ She should choose a small tin.

12. Look at the triangle below.

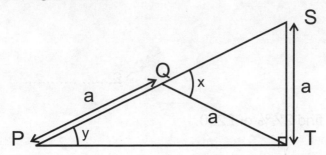

(DIAGRAM NOT TO SCALE)

(a) Explain carefully why x = 2y.

2 marks

(b) Find the value of y.

y = ...°

2 marks

13. (a) Calculate 10% of £200.

£ 20

1 mark

(b) Use your answer to (a) to find 2½% of £200.

$10\% = £20$
$2\% = £4$
$1\% = £2$
$\frac{1}{2}\% = £1$

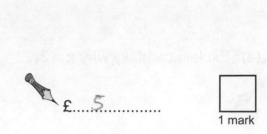

£ 5

1 mark

(c) In Meanland, there is a tax of 22½% on every item that is sold.
A television costs £220 before tax.

Work out how much it costs including the tax.

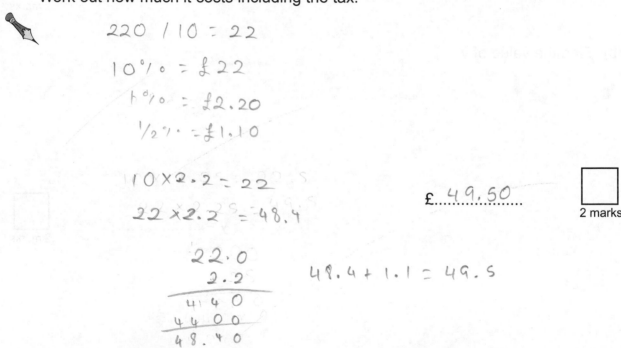

$220 / 10 = 22$
$10\% = £22$
$5\% = £2.20$
$\frac{1}{2}\% = £1.10$

$10 \times 2.2 = 22$
$22 \times 2.2 = 48.4$

$\begin{array}{r} 22.0 \\ 2.2 \\ \hline 4\ 4\ 0 \\ 4\ 4\ 0\ 0 \\ \hline 48.40 \end{array}$

$48.4 + 1.1 = 49.5$

£ 49.50

2 marks

14. Tick the statements that are true.

(a)
☐ When x is even, x(x + 3) is odd.
☑ When x is even, x(x + 3) is even.

☐ 1 mark

(b)
☑ When x is odd, $x^2 + 1$ is even.
☐ When x is odd, $x^2 + 1$ is odd.

☐ 1 mark

(c)
☐ $x^2 + x$ is always odd.
☑ $x^2 + x$ is always even.

☐ 1 mark

15. I have a list of five numbers.

The mean of the numbers is 4.

The mode of the numbers is 2.

The median of the numbers is 3.

Write down one possibility for my list of numbers.

median

2, 2, 3, 6, 7

mode

$4 \times 5 = 20$

$2 + 2 + 3 + 6 + 7 = 20$

☐ 2 marks

16. (a) Find the area of the trapezium below.

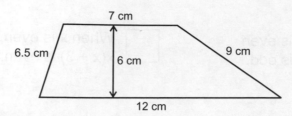

7 cm

6.5 cm

6 cm

9 cm

12 cm

$$\frac{7+12}{2} \times 6 \qquad 9.5 \times 6 = 57$$

$$\frac{19}{2} = 9.5$$

.... cm²

2 marks

(b) This prism has the trapezium from part (a) as its cross-section.

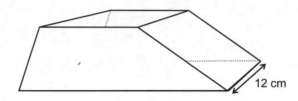

12 cm

Find its volume.

.... cm³

2 marks

17. In a science experiment, Sabiha investigated the relationship between temperature and time taken for a chemical reaction to finish.

She plotted a graph of her results.

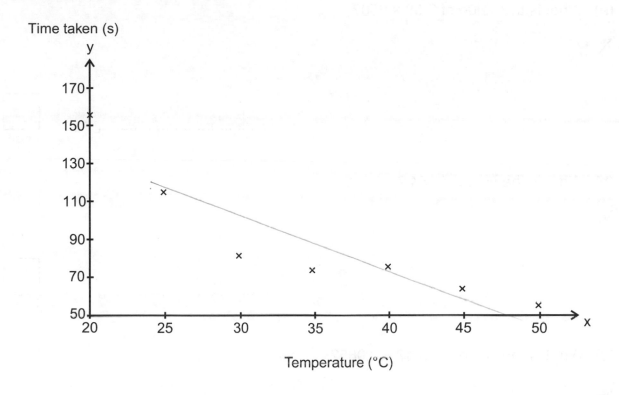

(a) What type of correlation does the graph show?

....Weak..negative...

(b) Sabiha thought the equation of the line of best fit was y = 3x + 20.

Give two reasons why this cannot be correct.

y = 3x+20 means it would intercept the
y axis at 20 but 20 is not present in on the y axis
this graph.

the gradient is also a positive but the
graph has a negative correlation
to the gradient should be
a negative.

18. Use the following calculation to answer the questions below.

$$23.8 \times 6.5 = 154.7$$

(a) What is the value of 2.38 × 650?

............1547............

(b) What is the value of 154.7 ÷ 238?

............0.65............

(c) What is the value of 15.47 ÷ 0.065?

............0.00238............

END OF TEST

Key Stage 3

Mathematics Test

Practice Paper 3B
Calculator allowed

Maths

KEY STAGE
3

PRACTICE PAPER
3B

Read this page, but don't open the booklet until your teacher says you can start. Write your name and school in the spaces below.

First Name _____

Last Name _____

School _____

Remember

- The test is one hour long.

- Make sure you have these things with you before you start:
  pen, pencil, rubber, ruler, calculator, angle measurer or
  protractor and pair of compasses.
  You may use tracing paper.

- There are some formulas you might need on the next page.

- The easier questions are at the start of the test.

- Try to answer all of the questions.

- Don't use any rough paper — write all your answers and
  working in this test paper.

- Check your work carefully before the end of the test.

- If you're not sure what to do, ask your teacher.

Instructions

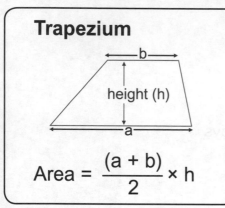 This means write down your answer or show your working and your answer.

 You may use a calculator in this test.

Formulas

Trapezium

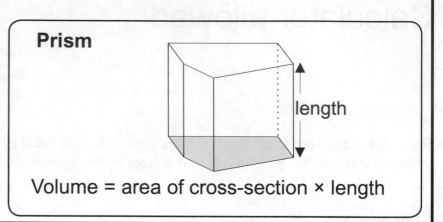

Area = $\dfrac{(a + b)}{2} \times h$

Prism

Volume = area of cross-section × length

---

1. Calculate the value of each of the expressions below when x = -2.

(a) 4 + x =  ....2...........

 1 mark

(b) 5x =  ....-10.........

 1 mark

(c) $2x^2$ =  ....8.........

 1 mark

2. I am going on holiday and need to buy some euros.

BetaTravel offers 82 euros for £60

BestXchange offers 100 euros for £72

(a) Which gives the better value for money?
You must show your working.

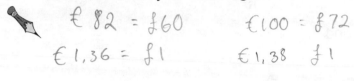

€ 82 = £60   €100 = £72
€ 1,36 = £1   €1,38 £1

1.36 < 1.38

.....Best X change   ☐
                          2 marks

(b) Calculate how many euros I would get for £100 at BestXChange.

€100 = £72

€1,38 = £1

€138 = £100

.........138......... euros   ☐
                          1 mark

3. Look at the diagram. The lines marked with arrows are parallel.
PQ and QR are the same length.

(DIAGRAM NOT
TO SCALE)

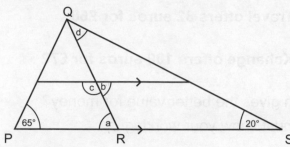

Work out the size of the angles a, b, c and d.

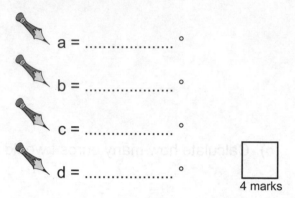

a = ... °

b = ... °

c = ... °

d = ... °

4 marks

4. (a) Write down the nth term for this number sequence:

1, 4, 9, 16, 25, ...

 ......n^2........

1 mark

Use your answer to work out the nth term for these number sequences:

(b) **2, 5, 10, 17, 26, ...**

 ....

1 mark

(c) **3, 12, 27, 48, 75, ...**

 ....

1 mark

(d) **3, 9, 19, 33, 51, ...**

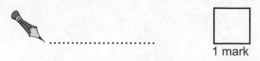 ....

1 mark

5. A goat has a rope attached to its collar.

The length of the rope is 6 metres.

The other end of the rope is attached to the outside of the shed as shown.

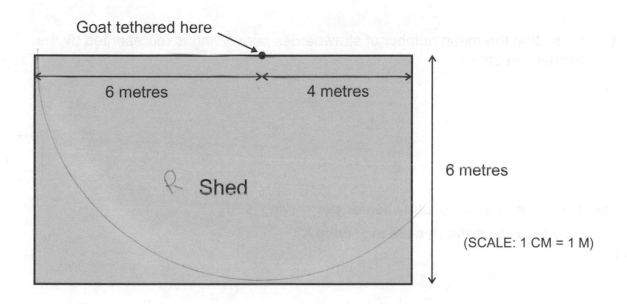

Goat tethered here

6 metres

4 metres

6 metres

R Shed

(SCALE: 1 CM = 1 M)

Show accurately on the diagram the region where the goat could be.

Label the region R.

2 marks

6. Joe buys 3 servings of strawberries at the Wimbledon Lawn Tennis Championships.
The number of strawberries in each serving are given by the expressions below.

Serving	Number of strawberries
A	2n
B	n + 5
C	3n – 2

(a) Write an expression for the total number of strawberries in the
3 servings. Show your working.

.... $6n + 3$ ....

1 mark

(b) Show that the mean number of strawberries per serving is represented by the
expression 2n + 1.

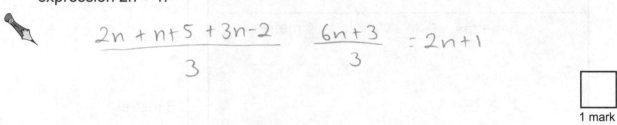

$$\frac{2n + n + 5 + 3n - 2}{3} \qquad \frac{6n + 3}{3} = 2n + 1$$

1 mark

(c) The mean number of strawberries per serving is 11.
How many strawberries are in serving A?

$$2n + 1 = 11$$
$$2n = 10$$
$$n = 5$$

.... 10 ....

2 marks

$$\frac{6n + 3}{3} \qquad \frac{30 + 3}{3} \qquad \frac{33}{3} = 11$$

7. I have three coins — a 2p, a 5p and a 10p.

    The 2p and 5p coins are equally likely to show a head or a tail.

    The 10p coin is biased so it is twice as likely to show a head as a tail.

    I throw all three coins.

    What is the probability I get the same on all of them?

    ....

    [ ] 3 marks

8. Harry has started weight-training.

    Since he started, his weight has increased by $\frac{1}{16}$. $= \frac{6.25}{100}$
    He now weighs 76.5 kg.

    How much did he weigh before he started?

    76.5 = 106.25%

    .... kg

    [ ] 2 marks

9. In the table below there are statements on the left hand side and expressions for someone's age, in years, on the right hand side.
The letter B represents Bill's age in years.

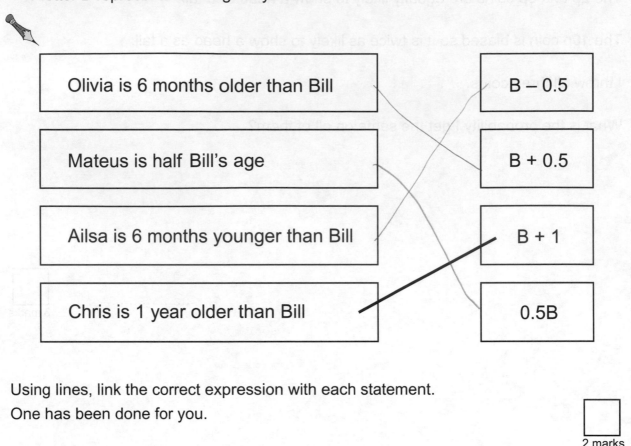

Olivia is 6 months older than Bill	B − 0.5
Mateus is half Bill's age	B + 0.5
Ailsa is 6 months younger than Bill	B + 1
Chris is 1 year older than Bill	0.5B

Using lines, link the correct expression with each statement.
One has been done for you.

2 marks

10. Multiply out the expressions below.

Write your answers as simply as possible.

(a) $3(x - 3) - 2(3 - 2x)$

$3x - 9 - 6 - 4x$

$-x - 15$

.... $-x - 15$ ....

2 marks

(b) $(2x - 1)(x - 3)$

$2x^2 - 6x - x + 3$

$2x^2 - 7x + 3$

.... $2x^2 - 7x + 3$ ....

2 marks

11. Anjum, Billie and Catie are eating sweets.

The ratio of the number Anjum eats to the number Billie eats is 3 : 5.
The ratio of the number Billie eats to the number Catie eats is 4 : 7.
Catie eats 70 sweets.

How many sweets do the three children eat altogether?

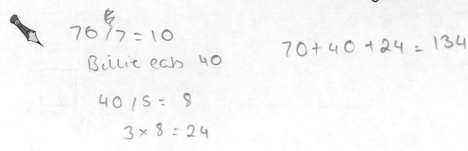

$$70 / 7 = 10$$
Billie eats 40

$$70 + 40 + 24 = 134$$

$$40 / 5 = 8$$
$$3 \times 8 = 24$$

...............134...............

2 marks

12. Fill in the missing numbers:

(a) 150 mm is the same as .....0.15... m.

1 mark

(b) 150 mm² is the same as .... m².

1 mark

(c) The length of a piece of wood is 150 mm to the nearest 10 mm.

The actual length lies between .....145... mm and .....154... mm.

1 mark

13. The frequency table shows the number of days that 30 pupils were off sick from school in a year.

Number of days sick	Frequency
0 - 4	14
5 - 9	8
10 - 14	5
15 - 19	3

(a) Which is the modal group?

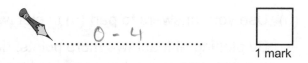

.............0 - 4............ ☐ 1 mark

(b) Estimate the mean number of days that pupils were off sick.

.... ☐ 3 marks

(c) Explain why you can only find an estimate of the mean.

☐ 1 mark

14. Some exam-markers get paid £2 for each paper they mark.

Anna takes 20 minutes to mark each paper.
David takes 15 minutes to mark each paper.

(a) Work out how much Anna and David earn per hour.

 Anna earns £..........6......... per hour

David earns £...........?........ per hour

(b) Use your answers to part (a) to plot two points on the grid below.

By plotting at least two more points, draw a graph to show the relationship between amount earned per hour and the time taken to mark each paper.

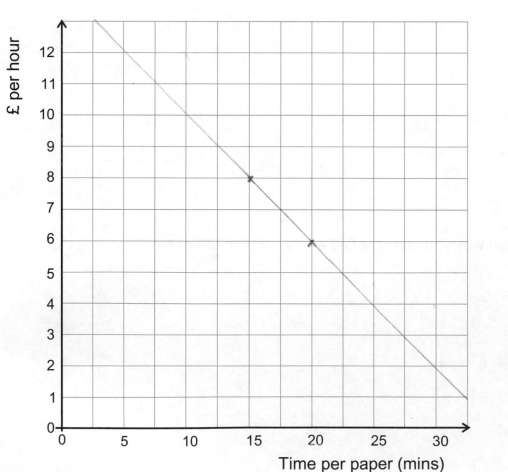

15. (a) In a test, Jamie answered 40% of the questions.
He got 50% of the questions he answered right.
Manjinder answered 50% of the questions and got 40% of them right.
Manjinder said "That means we got the same mark."

Is Manjinder right or wrong? Explain your answer.

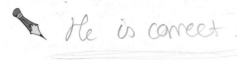 He is correct.

2 marks

(b) In a sale, a shop reduced all its prices by 10%.
After the sale, the shop manager increased the prices by 10%.
A customer said "That means the prices are now the same as they were before the sale."

Is the customer right or wrong? Explain your answer.

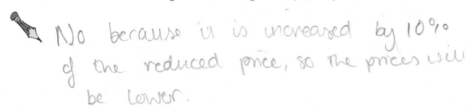 No because it is increased by 10% of the reduced price, so the prices will be lower.

2 marks

(c) At Mary's local garage, the price of a litre of petrol rose by 20% in April, then by another 20% in May.
Mary said "That's a 40% rise in two months."

Is Mary right or wrong? Explain your answer.

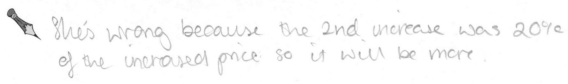 She's wrong because the 2nd increase was 20% of the increased price so it will be more.

2 marks

16. David reads in the paper that the dice produced at one factory are more likely to land on a six than on any of the other numbers.

To investigate this he buys 20 dice.
He throws all 20 dice together 12 times.
He counts the number of sixes he gets each time.

The table shows his results.

Throw	1	2	3	4	5	6	7	8	9	10	11	12
Number of sixes	1	3	5	2	4	6	3	4	6	0	4	4

(a) Use David's results to estimate the probability of getting a six using these dice.

240
42

42/240 = 0.175

 ...0.175....

[ ] 1 mark

(b) David decides from his investigation that the paper is right.
Do you agree? Explain your answer.

No because they landed on 6, 42/240 times and that is much less that a majority.

[ ] 1 mark

17. The diagram shows the cross-section of a marquee fixed on horizontal ground.

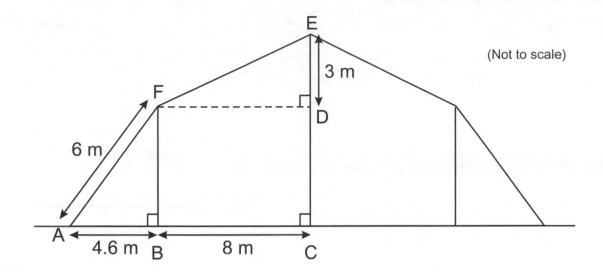

(Not to scale)

BF and CE are vertical supports.

AB = 4.6 m, AF = 6 m, DE = 3 m and BC = 8 m.

(a) Which expression represents the length of EF in metres?
Circle the correct answer.

$$3^2 + 8^2 \qquad \sqrt{3^2 + 8^2} \qquad \sqrt{(3 + 8)^2} \qquad \sqrt{3} + \sqrt{8} \qquad \sqrt{3^2 - 8^2}$$

1 mark

(b) Work out the length of BF to 3 significant figures.

$6^2 - 4.6^2 = 14.84$

$\sqrt{14.84} = 3.85$

................3.85................ cm

2 marks

18. A cylinder has radius r, height h, and a volume of 36π cm^3.
r and h are both whole numbers.

Write down two possible sets of values for r and h.

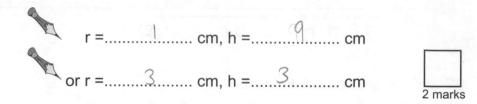

r =...........1.......... cm, h =..............9.......... cm

or r =..........3.......... cm, h =.........3.......... cm

2 marks

19. In the diagram below, triangles ABE and ACD are similar.

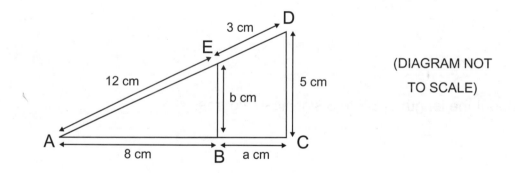

D

3 cm

E

12 cm

5 cm

b cm

(DIAGRAM NOT
TO SCALE)

A

8 cm

B   a cm

C

Find the lengths a and b.

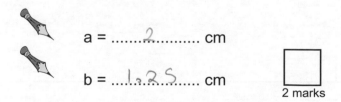

a = ...2.......... cm

b = ...1.25..... cm

2 marks

END OF TEST

Answers
KS3 Maths Paper 1A Calculator NOT Allowed

Q	Marks	Correct answer	The bit in the middle tells you how to get to the answer	Useful tips

1. a | 1 | **53°** | Angles A and C are the same.

b | 2 | **127°** | Angles B and D are the same, so B = (360 − 53 − 53) ÷ 2 = 254 ÷ 2 = 127°.
(2 marks for correct answer, otherwise 1 mark for some correct working.)

---

2. a | 1 | **700, 0.7** | 1 cm³ = 1 ml, so 700 cm³ = 700 ml. 1000 ml = 1 litre, so 700 ml ÷ 1000 = 0.7 litres.

b | 1 | **63, 0.063** | 1000 g = 1 kg, so 63000 g ÷ 1000 = 63 kg. 1000 kg = 1 tonne, so 63 kg ÷ 1000 = 0.063 tonnes.

---

3. | 2

(2 marks for correct answer, otherwise 1 mark for correct enlargement but wrong position.)

TIP: A scale factor of ½ means the lines on your new shape should be half as long, and each point should be half the distance from the centre.

---

4. | 2

	Theme Park	Seaside	Total
Boys	41	**23**	**64**
Girls	**42**	14	56
Total	**83**	**37**	120

(2 marks for correctly completed table, otherwise 1 mark for at least three correct values.)

---

5. a | 1 | **Both Julia and Gazza are correct.** | The expressions are the same. Two lengths of n and two of 10.

b | 2 | **4n + 10** | $2n + 2n + 5 + 5 = 4n + 10$. One mark for this working.

c | 2 | **n + 40** | $\frac{n}{2} + \frac{n}{2} + 4 \times 10 = n + 40$. One mark for a correct expression and one for simplifying.

d | 1 | **n = 10** | The perimeters are equal when $n + 40 = 4n + 10$. $3n = 30$. $n = 10$

TIPS: Don't worry about n, it just stands for any number.

---

6. | 4

6		21		25	
3	54	18	7	84	12
9		4		5	

12.5 5³ 10
5

(4 marks for all six correct values, otherwise 3 marks for five correct, 2 marks for four correct or 1 mark for two or three correct.)

---

7. | 2 | **64 minutes** | £8.96 = 896p, 896 ÷ 14 = 64 minutes.
(2 marks for correct answer, otherwise 1 mark for some correct working.)

---

8. a | 1 | **x = -6** | $\frac{3x}{9} = -2$, 3x = -18, x = -6

b | 1 | **y = 15** | 2y − 6 = 24, 2y = 30, y = 15

TIP: Always check your answers by putting them back into the equations.

c | 2 | **z = 18** | 3z − 7 = 29 + z, 3z − z = 29 + 7, 2z = 36, z = 18
(2 marks for correct answer, otherwise 1 mark for some correct working.)

---

9. a | 1 | **25%** | $\frac{90}{360} \times 100 = 25\%$

b | 2 | **216°** | $\frac{60}{100} \times 360 = 216°$

TIP: Remember — with pie charts, 360° always represents 100% of the data.

(2 marks for correct answer, otherwise 1 mark for some correct working.)

c	2	**2000**	100 – 25 – 60 = 15% of people are not registered with a dentist. 15% = 300 people. So 1% = 300 ÷ 15 = 20. 100% = 20 × 100 = 2000 people. **(2 marks for correct answer, otherwise 1 mark for some correct working.)**

---

10. a	1	$\dfrac{1}{4}$	$\dfrac{3}{4} - \dfrac{1}{2} = \dfrac{1}{4}$
b	2	$\dfrac{5}{8}$	$\dfrac{3}{4} + \dfrac{5}{8} + \dfrac{1}{2} = \dfrac{6}{8} + \dfrac{5}{8} + \dfrac{4}{8} = \dfrac{15}{8}$. $\dfrac{15}{8} \div 3 = \dfrac{5}{8}$ *TIP: To add fractions you need to put them over a* <u>*common denominator*</u>. **(2 marks for correct answer, otherwise 1 mark for finding the sum of the fractions.)**

11.	3	**24 teachers and 84 pupils**	2 + 7 = 9, so 1 part = 108 ÷ 9 = 12. 12 × 2 = 24 teachers, 12 × 7 = 84 pupils. **(3 marks for correct answer, otherwise 1 mark for some correct working and 1 mark for either 24 or 84.)**

---

12. a	2	**x = 12**	4x + 30 = 78, 4x = 78 – 30, 4x = 48, x = 12 **(1 mark for correct algebraic expression and 1 mark for correct answer.)**
b	1	**2008**	2020 – 12 = 2008

---

13. a	1	**-47**	y = (-2 × 25) + 3 = -47
b	1	**17**	-31 = -2x + 3, 2x = 34, x = 17 *TIP: You can also solve part (c) by using a simultaneous equations method.*
c	3	**(2.5, -2)**	-2x + 3 = 6x – 17, 3 + 17 = 6x + 2x, 20 = 8x, x = 2.5. So y = -2x + 3 = (-2 × 2.5) + 3 = -5 + 3 = -2. **(3 marks for a correct method and correct answer, otherwise 2 marks for a correct method and either x or y correct, or 1 mark for some correct working.)**

---

14. a	1	**0.68**	0.42 + 0.26 = 0.68
b	1	**0.32**	1 – (0.42 + 0.26) = 1 – 0.68 = 0.32 *TIP: All the probabilities must add up to 1.*
c	1	**21**	Number of peanuts = 0.42 × 50 = 21

15.	3	**15%**	0.75 × 0.2 = 0.15, 0.15 × 100 = 15% **(3 marks for correct answer, otherwise 1-2 marks for some correct working.)**

---

16. a	1	$d = \dfrac{e-6}{2}$	$2d + 6 = e$, $2d = e - 6$, $d = \dfrac{e-6}{2}$
b	2	$f = \sqrt{\dfrac{3g-8}{5}}$	$8 + 5f^2 = 3g$, $5f^2 = 3g - 8$, $f^2 = \dfrac{3g-8}{5}$, $f = \sqrt{\dfrac{3g-8}{5}}$ **(2 marks for correct answer, otherwise 1 mark for some correct working.)**

---

17. a	2	**0.03 × 0.1 = 0.003**	**(One mark for selecting the correct numbers)**
b	1	**20 ÷ 0.1 = 200**	Dividing by 0.1 is the same as multiplying by 10.
c	1	$\dfrac{2}{p}$	Dividing by a number between 0 and 1 is the same as multiplying by a number. So the result will be > 2 and therefore bigger than all the others.

---

18. a	2	**36 cm**	Ratio of kites = 25 : 10 = 5 : 2. 1 part = 90 ÷ 5 = 18 cm. 2 × 18 = 36 cm. **(2 marks for correct answer, otherwise 1 mark for some correct working.)**
b	1	**120°**	Similar shapes have the same angles.

KS3 Maths Paper 1B Calculator Allowed

Q	Marks	Correct answer	The bit in the middle tells you how to get to the answer	Useful tips

---

1.	a	1	**1.175768662**		
	b	1	**1.176**		TIP: Remember — you need to use <u>BODMAS</u> to tell the calculator which <u>order</u> to do things in.
	c	1	**3.2**		

2.	a	1	**Eight out of the twenty squares should be shaded.** $\frac{4}{10} = \frac{8}{20}$	
	b	1	**0.55**	22 out of 40 = 22 ÷ 40 = 0.55
	c	1	**62.5%**	40 out of 64, so (40 ÷ 64) × 100 = 62.5%

| 3. | a | 2 | **(2 marks for correct answer, otherwise 1 mark for at least 2 squares shaded correctly.)** |
| | b | 2 | or or or *TIP: When you've finished your pattern <u>turn the page round</u> through 360° and check that there are only two positions where it looks the same.* **(2 marks for correct answer, otherwise 1 mark for at least 2 squares shaded correctly.)** |

4.	a	1	$\dfrac{21}{40}$	There are 15 + 2 + 4 = 21 boys out of a total of 15 + 2 + 4 + 3 + 11 + 5 = 40 students.
	b	1	$\dfrac{9}{40}$	4 boys + 5 girls = 9 students play the keyboard out of a total of 40 students.
	c	1	$\dfrac{3}{18}$ or $\dfrac{1}{6}$	There are 3 girl guitarists out of a total of 15 boys + 3 girls = 18 students who play guitar.

5.	a	1	**£2.88**	36p × 8 = 288p = £2.88
	b	2	**Shop A by 9p**	At shop A it costs 36p × 18 = £6.48, at shop B it costs £2.19 × 3 = £6.57. £6.57 − £6.48 = 9p
			(2 marks for correct working and answer, otherwise 1 mark for getting both £6.48 and £6.57.)

| 6. | | 2 | **20 weeks** 105 − 77 = 28, 28 ÷ 1.4 = 20 weeks. |
| | | | **(2 marks for correct answer, otherwise 1 mark for some correct working.)** |

7.	a	1	**2s + 4**
	b	1	**11t² + 3t**
	c	1	**18u²**
	d	1	**4v²**

| 8. | a | 2 | | (2 marks for all six correct values, otherwise 1 mark for at least three.) |

Speed (s) in mph	frequency (f)	midpoint (x)	fx
90 < s ≤ 100	12	95	1140
100 < s ≤ 110	18	105	1890
110 < s ≤ 120	28	115	3220
120 < s ≤ 130	7	125	875
Total	65	-	7125

| | b | 1 | **109.6 mph** | 7125 ÷ 65 = 109.6 mph (to 1 d.p.) |

9.	4	**a = 50°, b = 40°, c = 200°, d = 70°**

$a = 360° − 130° − 90° − 90° = 50°$. $b = 130° − 90° = 40°$.
$c = 360° − 160° = 200°$. $d = 180° − 110° = 70°$.

(1 mark for each correct angle.)

TIP: These questions shouldn't cause any bother if you've learnt the angle rules.

---

10. a	2	**£350**

£287 is 100% − 18% = 82% of the original price. 1% = 287 ÷ 82 = 3.5, so 100% = 3.5 × 100 = £350.
(2 marks for correct answer, otherwise 1 mark for some correct working.)

b	2	**55%**

120 − 54 = 66 photos are discarded, $\frac{66}{120} \times 100 = 55\%$.

(2 marks for correct answer, otherwise 1 mark for some correct working.)

11.	2	**339.3 cm³**

Volume = $\pi r^2 h = \pi \times 3^2 \times 12 = 339.3$ cm³ (to 1 d.p.)
(2 marks for correct answer, otherwise 1 mark for substituting correctly into the formula.)

12.	2	**5.7 seconds**

Time = distance/speed, so the times are 40 ÷ 12.5 = 3.2 and 40 ÷ 16 = 2.5. 3.2 + 2.5 = 5.7 s.
(2 marks for correct answer, otherwise 1 mark for either 3.2 or 2.5.)

13.	3	**24 newspapers**

Let x = number of newspapers delivered on Tuesday. So 3.5x + 30 = 114, 3.5x = 114 − 30 = 84, x = 24.

(3 marks for correct answer, otherwise 1 mark for correct equation and 1 mark for attempting to solve it.)

14.	2	**x² + 3x − 28**

$(x + 7)(x − 4) = x^2 − 4x + 7x − 28 = x^2 + 3x − 28$.

(2 marks for correct answer, otherwise 1 mark for getting 2 out of 3 terms correct.)

---

15. a	1	**P is (0 , 1). Q is (1 , 3)**

b	2	**2**

Gradient of line = change in y ÷ change in x = (3 − 1) ÷ (1 − 0) = 2 ÷ 1 = 2.
(2 marks for correct answer, or 1 mark for using the correct method but getting the wrong answer.)

c	1	**y = 2x + 1**

The gradient is 2 and it crosses the y-axis at 1, so the equation must be y = 2x + 1.

---

16. a	2	**Body mass index = 22.9 (3 s.f.) or 22.86 (4 s.f.), Weight status = Normal**

Body mass index = $70 \div 1.75^2 = 22.857...$
(1 mark for correct body mass index, 1 mark for correct weight status.)

b	2	**1.70 m**

$h^2 = 55 \div 19 = 2.8947...$, $h = \sqrt{2.8947...} = 1.70$ m (2 d.p.)
(2 marks for correct answer, otherwise 1 mark for some correct working.)

c	3	**11 kg**

For body mass index of 28, weight = 28 × 1.64² = 75.3088 kg.
For body mass index of 24, weight = 24 × 1.64² = 64.5504 kg.
Weight loss = 75.3088 − 64.5504 = 10.7584 = 11 kg (to nearest kilogram).

(3 marks for correct answer, otherwise 1 mark for each correct weight.)

---

17. a	2	**78 m**

$(AB)^2 = 30^2 + 72^2 = 900 + 5184 = 6084$, $AB = \sqrt{6084} = 78$ m

(2 marks for correct answer, otherwise 1 mark for some correct working.)

b	2	**22.6°**

$a = \tan^{-1}\left(\frac{30}{72}\right) = 22.6°$

(2 marks for correct answer, otherwise 1 mark for some correct working.)

---

18. a	1	**0.4**	1 − 0.6 = 0.4
b	1	**12 days**	0.4 × 30 = 12
c	1	**0.216**	0.6 × 0.6 × 0.6 = 0.216

TIP: To work out the expected number of days you just multiply the probability for one day by the total number of days. Easy.

KS3 Maths Paper 2A Calculator NOT Allowed

Q	Marks	Correct answer	*The bit in the middle tells you how to get to the answer*	*Useful tips*
1. a	1	**4/15**	There are four raspberry flavour out of a total of fifteen.	
b	1	**9/15 or 3/5**	There are nine sweets that are not blackberry out of fifteen.	
c	1	**Cannot tell. You don't know how many sweets are in his bag so you don't know if half of them is more or less than the 5 Debbie has.**		
			(Only award mark for "Cannot tell" <u>and</u> a correct explanation.)	

2. a	3		To construct the triangle draw the base the correct length first.
			Use compasses set to 5 cm and 4 cm from each end of the base to draw arcs.
			Where the arcs cross gives the position for B.
			(3 marks for correct answer, otherwise 2 marks for two sides the correct length, or 1 mark for one side the correct length.)
b	1	**40 – 43°**	

3.	2	**£115**	Use 50 as an estimate of the number of calculators and £2.30 as an estimate of the cost. So 2.30 × 50 = 2.30 × 10 × 5 = 23 × 5 = £115. **(2 marks for correct answer (also accept 2 × 50 = £100), otherwise 1 mark for evidence of sensible rounding.)**

4. a	1	**£99**	(7 × 12) + 15 = 84 + 15 = £99
b	2	**11 days**	Work backwards through the number machine: 147 – 15 = 132, 132 ÷ 12 = 11. **(2 marks for correct answer, otherwise 1 mark for some correct working.)**
c	1	**The delivery charge**	

5. a	1	**x = 6**	3x + 7 = 25, 3x = 18, x = 18 ÷ 3 = 6	*TIP: There are several different methods for solving equations.*
b	1	**x = 9.5**	4(x – 2) = 30, 4x – 8 = 30, 4x = 38, x = 9.5	*Trial and error can work well for simple ones like part (a). But for more complicated ones you really need to know how*
c	1	**x = -4**	2x – 9 = 5x + 3, -3x = 12, x = -4	*to <u>multiply out brackets</u> and <u>collect like terms</u>.*

6. a	1	**-5**	
b	1	**-3**	*TIP: Remember the <u>rules</u> for adding and subtracting <u>negative numbers</u> —*
c	1	**4**	*" + +" and " – –" mean add, but " + –" means subtract.*
d	1	**12**	

7. a	1	**144 cm³**	6 × 6 × 4 = 144 cm³
b	2	**168 cm²**	Area of side faces = 6 × 4 = 24. Area of top and bottom faces = 6 × 6 = 36. Total surface area = (4 × 24) + (2 × 36) = 96 + 72 = 168 cm².
			(2 marks for correct answer, otherwise 1 mark for some correct working.)
c	2		**(2 marks for correct answer (the cuboids can be drawn in different positions), otherwise 1 mark for a cuboid with two dimensions correct.)**
			TIP: The easiest way to think about this is that the volume of a 2 cm cube is 2³ = 8 cm³. So to make a cuboid of volume 48 cm³, you need 48 ÷ 8 = 6 cubes.

OR

8. a	1	**20%**	3 + 5 + 2 = 10, (2 ÷ 10) × 100 = 20%
b	2	**30 geese, 12 swans**	18 ducks are 3 parts of the bird population, so 1 part is 18 ÷ 3 = 6. Geese = 5 × 6 = 30, swans = 2 × 6 = 12 **(1 mark for each correct answer.)**

9. a	3	**0.2, 0.3, 2/5 , 1/2**	Turn the fractions into decimals: 1 ÷ 2 = 0.5. 2 ÷ 5 = 0.4. So the order is 0.2, 0.3, 2/5, 1/2. **(1 mark for 0.2 first, 1 mark for 1/2 last, 1 mark for middle terms in correct order.)**

| 10. | 2 | | | (2 marks matching all five expressions correctly, 1 mark for matching three or four options correctly.) |

Matching boxes:
1, 2, 3, 4 / 1, 4, 9, 16 / 2, 5, 8, 11 / 4, 7, 10, 13 / −2, −4, −6, −8 / −4, −1, 4, 11

to: n^2 / $-2n$ / n / $3n - 1$ / $n^2 - 5$ / $3n + 1$

| 11. a | 1 | **50°F** | $F = \dfrac{9C}{5} + 32 = \dfrac{9 \times 10}{5} + 32 = 18 + 32 = 50°F$ |

TIP: When you're working things out without a calculator remember to simplify as much as possible. $(9 \times -20) \div 5$ becomes a lot easier if you cancel the 5 first. Then it's just 9×-4 which is -36.

| b | 2 | **-4°F** | $F = \dfrac{9C}{5} + 32 = \dfrac{9 \times -20}{5} + 32 = -36 + 32 = -4°F$ |

(2 marks for correct answer, otherwise 1 mark for substituting -20 into formula but then making one error.)

| c | 2 | $C = \dfrac{5(F - 32)}{9}$ | $F = \dfrac{9C}{5} + 32$, $F - 32 = \dfrac{9C}{5}$, $5(F - 32) = 9C$, $C = \dfrac{5(F - 32)}{9}$ |

(2 marks for correct answer, otherwise 1 mark for completing the first step to get $F - 32 = \dfrac{9C}{5}$.)

| 12. | 2 | **No. The numbers do not fit Pythagoras' Theorem. $6^2 = 36$ but $5^2 + 4^2 = 25 + 16 = 41$.** |

(2 marks for No and correct explanation, otherwise 1 mark for showing use of Pythagoras' Theorem.)

| 13. | 2 | $x^2 + 9x + 20$ | $(x + 5)(x + 4) = x^2 + 4x + 5x + 20 = x^2 + 9x + 20$ |

TIP: You'll have no trouble with these if you've learnt the foolproof FOIL method.

(2 marks for correct answer, otherwise 1 mark for an unsimplified expression with at least three terms correct.)

| 14. a | 2 |

	1	2	3	4	5	6
1	1	2	3	4	5	6
2	2	4	6	8	10	12
3	3	6	9	12	15	18

(2 marks for all twelve correct values, otherwise 1 mark for at least six correct values.)

| b | 1 | **6/18 or 1/3** | Six out of the eighteen scores are odd. |

| 15. | 3 | **x = 1.5 and y = 3** | The perimeter of the triangle is 36, so because it's an equilateral triangle, every side must be 36 ÷ 3 - 12. So 8x = 12, which gives x = 12 ÷ 8 = 1.5. Then 2x + 3y = 12 = (2 × 1.5) + 3y = 12, or 3y = 9, giving y = 3. |

(3 marks for the correct answers. If an answer is wrong, then 1 mark for finding the length of each side ad 1 mark for each x and y.)

| 16. a | 3 |

Number of cakes per box	100	250	500	1000	2000	5000
Number of boxes	100	40	20	10	5	2

100 ÷ 4 = 250.   100000 ÷ 10 = 1000

10000 ÷ 100 = 100   10000 ÷ 2000 = 5

| b | 1 | **T = N × B** | The batch of cakes has to be put into N boxes, each containing B cakes. |
| c | 2 | **3 hours 20 minutes** | 10000 ÷ 50 = 200 minutes = 2 hours and 20 minutes. |

| 17. a | 1 | **29030** | |
| b | 2 | 2.462×10^4 | $29030 - 4410 = 24620 = 2.462 \times 10^4$ |

(2 marks for correct answer, otherwise 1 mark for correct calculation but answer not in standard form.)

---

18. a	1	**y = 0**	Anything to the power 0 is 1.
b	1	**y = 4**	
c	1	**y = 2**	$72 = y^3 \times 3^2$, $y^3 = 72 \div 9 = 8$, $\sqrt[3]{8} = 2$

TIP: Parts (b) and (c) look tricky, but don't panic — you can work them out by trial and error. Sub in values of y (1, 2, etc.) and you soon get the right answer.

KS3 Maths Paper 2B Calculator Allowed

Q	Marks	Correct answer	The bit in the middle tells you how to get to the answer	Useful tips

1. a 1
b 1

TIP: With <u>rotations</u>, use tracing paper to help find the centre of rotation.
With <u>reflections</u>, each point of the new shape should be <u>exactly the same distance</u> away from the mirror line as the corresponding point of the old shape.

---

2. 3

Number of 5p coins	Number of 10p coins	Number of 20p coins
1	0	2
1	2	1
3	1	1
5	0	1
1	4	0
2	3	0
5	2	0
7	1	0
9	0	0

(3 marks for all eight different ways, otherwise 2 marks for five to seven ways or 1 mark for at least three ways.)

---

3. a 1 E.g.

4/7 × 21 = 12 (shade any 12 squares)

b 1 E.g.

0.3 × 20 = 6 (shade any 6 squares)

c 1 E.g.

45/100 × 20 = 9 (shade any 9 squares)

TIP: Just count the number of squares and times by the proportion. Easy!

---

4. a 1 **35 minutes** 52 − 17 = 35
b 1 **31 minutes** order list: 17 26 31 43 52, middle number = 31.
c 2 E.g. **20 23 25 30 40 (1 mark for a list with 25 as the median, 1 mark for a list with a range of 20.)**

---

5. a 2 **30** 108 ÷ 9 = 12° per student. 360° ÷ 12 = 30
(2 marks for correct answer, otherwise 1 mark for some correct working.)

b 1 **Cannot tell**
A bigger proportion of 9A have dogs, but you don't know how many students are in 9B.
(Only award the mark for "Cannot tell" and a correct explanation.)

---

6. a 2 E.g. **(0, 7), (1, 6), (2, 5)**
(2 marks for three pairs that fit the rule, otherwise 1 mark for two pairs that fit the rule.)

b 2

TIP: In part (a) you handily found three points on the line x + y = 7. So just plot them and join with a straight line.

(1 mark for plotting at least three correct points and 1 mark for joining them with a straight line.)

---

7. 2

Keeping your compass setting the same, draw two arcs from each cross. Draw a straight line between the two points where the arcs cross. This is the perpendicular bisector.
(2 marks for correct answer, otherwise 1 mark for drawing arcs (or circles) to give at least two points on the locus.)

---

8. a 2 **11.2%** Increase in salary = £3600, (3600 ÷ 32 200) × 100 = 11.180... = 11.2% (1 d.p.).
(2 marks for correct answer, otherwise 1 mark for 3600.)

b 2 **£26 542** 28 400 = 107%, so 1% = 28 400 ÷ 107 = 265.4205..., so 100% = 100 × 265.4205... = 26 542.05...
= £26 542 (nearest £) **(2 marks for correct answer, otherwise 1 mark for some correct working.)**

9.	a	1	**28**	$4 + 9 + 8 + 5 + 2 = 28$

	b	3	**6 hours and 40 minutes**

Multiply all frequencies by the mid values of the groups: $(4 \times 1.5) + (9 \times 4.5) + (8 \times 7.5) + (5 \times 10.5) + (2 \times 13.5) =$ 186, $186 \div 28 = 6.642...$ hours. $0.642...$ hours $\times 60 = 38.57...$ mins, so 6 hours 40 mins to the nearest 10 mins.

(3 marks for correct answer. Otherwise 2 marks for correct calculations but answer not rounded, or 1 mark for getting 186.)

10.	a	2	**10**

Circumference $= 2\pi r = 2\pi = 6.28...$ cm. $65 \div 6.28... = 10.34...$, so 10 complete revolutions.
(2 marks for correct answer, otherwise 1 mark for correctly finding circumference.)

	b	2	**3.14 cm²**

Area $= \pi r^2 = \pi \times 1^2 = 3.14$ cm² (3 s.f.)
(2 marks for correct answer, or 1 mark for using correct formula but with a calculation error.)

	c	3	**43**

Radius of real wheel $= \sqrt{(0.58 \div \pi)} = 0.429...$ m $= 0.43$ m (2 d.p.).
Radius of toy wheel $= 1$ cm $= 0.01$ m. So scale factor $= 0.43 \div 0.01 = 43$.
(3 marks for correct answer, otherwise 1 mark for finding radius of real wheel and 1 mark for finding radius of toy wheel in same units as real wheel.)

11.	a	1	**18°**	$180° - 162° = 18°$

	b	1	**20**	$360° \div 18° = 20$ sides

*TIP: Remember the **rule**: exterior angle = 360° ÷ no. of sides. So just rearrange to find the number of sides.*

12.	a	1	**30.9 mph**	$\dfrac{18}{35} \times 60 = 30.9$ mph (3 s.f.)

	b	1	**28.4 minutes**	$\dfrac{18}{38} \times 60 = 28.4$ minutes (3 s.f.)

TIP: Watch out with these. You need to multiply or divide by 60 to change the time from minutes into hours or vice versa.

	c	1	**16.7 miles**	$\dfrac{25}{60} \times 40 = 16.7$ miles (3 s.f.)

13.	a	2	**x = 8.05 cm**	$x^2 = 3.4^2 + 7.3^2 = 64.85$, $\sqrt{64.85} = 8.05$ cm (3 s.f.)

(2 marks for correct answer, otherwise 1 mark for correct use of Pythagoras' theorem.)

	b	2	**x = 2.68 cm**	$x^2 = 6.3^2 - 5.7^2 = 7.2$, $\sqrt{7.2} = 2.68$ cm (3 s.f.)

(2 marks for correct answer, otherwise 1 mark for correct use of Pythagoras' theorem.)

14.	a	2	**195.4 cm³**	$V = \dfrac{4}{3} \times \pi \times 3.6^3 = 195.432... = 195$ cm³ (3 s.f.)

(2 marks for correct answer, otherwise 1 mark for correct substitution into formula.)

	b	2	**1.89 cm**	$r = \sqrt[3]{\dfrac{3V}{4\pi}} = \sqrt[3]{\dfrac{3 \times 28.3}{4\pi}} = \sqrt[3]{6.756} = 1.89$ cm (3 s.f.)

(2 marks for correct answer, otherwise 1 mark for correctly rearranging formula for r.)

15.	a	2	**a = 21.3°**	$\tan a = \dfrac{4.8}{12.3}$, $a = \tan^{-1}\left(\dfrac{4.8}{12.3}\right) = 21.317... = 21.3°$ (3 s.f.)

(2 marks for correct answer, otherwise 1 mark for use of tan.)

	b	2	**b = 2.60 cm**	$\sin 32° = b/4.9$, so $b = \sin 32° \times 4.9 = 2.596... = 2.60$ cm (3 s.f.)

(2 marks for correct answer, otherwise 1 mark for use of sin.)

16.	a	2	**3a + 2c = 31, 2a + 5c = 39**	(1 mark for each equation.)

	b	2	**a = £7, c = £5**

To get 6a in both equations, multiply the first by 2 and the second by 3 to get $6a + 4c = 62$ and $6a + 15c = 117$. Now subtract the first from the second to get $11c = 55$ and so $c = 5$.
$3a + 2c = 31$, so $3a = 21$ and $a = 7$.
(2 marks for correct working and answer, otherwise 1 mark for some correct working and either a or c.)

17.	a	2	**x = 4.8 cm, y = 8.75 cm**

From rectangle B, ratio of length and width is $8 \div 5 = 1.6$. $x = 3 \times 1.6 = 4.8$ cm and $y = 14 \div 1.6 = 8.75$ cm.   **(1 mark for each correct length.)**

	b	1	**12/35 or 0.34**

A is smaller than C so the scale factor is less than 1. $4.8 \div 14 = 48/140 = 12/35$ (or 0.34 (2 s.f.)).
(2 marks for correct answer, otherwise 1 mark for some correct working.)

KS3 Maths Paper 3A Calculator NOT Allowed

Q	Marks	Correct answer	*The bit in the middle tells you how to get to the answer*	*Useful tips*

1. a | 1 | $8 \times 30 = 240$, $8 \times 7 = 56$, $240 + 56 = 296$ (or do a multiplication showing that a 5 must be carried).

b | 2 | **1184** | 32×37 is 4 lots of 8×37, 4×296 is $4 \times (300 - 4) = 1200 - 16 = 1184$.
(2 marks for correct answer, otherwise 1 mark for saying that you need to find 4 lots of 296, or trying to do that multiplication sum.)

2. a | 1 | **d + 10**
b | 1 | **k − 7**
c | 1 | **3d**
d | 1 | **3d − d = 2d**
e | 2 | **2d − k** | The difference between their ages is d − k, so in d − k years time Katya will be David's age now. His age then is d + d − k, which is 2d − k.
(2 marks for correct answer, otherwise 1 mark for getting d − k.)

3. | 2 | **10 cm** | Area = ½ × base × height. So 100 = ½ × 20 × height, or 100 = 10 × height. So height = 100 ÷ 10 = 10 cm. **(One mark only for correct working but wrong answer.)**

4. a | 2 | **No — Because some multiples of 3 are even, e.g. 6.**
(1 mark for saying no, and 1 mark for the correct explanation.)
b | 2 | **"It is a multiple of 3" and "It is divisible by 6" should be ticked.**
(2 marks for correct answer, otherwise 1 mark for 1 correct and 1 wrong statement ticked.)

5. a | 1 | **11** | The number of grey crosses is one more than the pattern number.
b | 1 | **20** | The number of white crosses is double the pattern number.
c | 1 | **301** | 101 grey + 200 white = 301 crosses altogether.

6. a | 1 | $\dfrac{12}{35}$ | $\dfrac{1}{7} + \dfrac{1}{5} = \dfrac{5}{35} + \dfrac{7}{35} = \dfrac{12}{35}$

b | 1 | $\dfrac{4}{39}$ | $\dfrac{2}{13} - \dfrac{2}{39} = \dfrac{6}{39} - \dfrac{2}{39} = \dfrac{4}{39}$

TIP: Don't always just times the two denominators — you're looking for the smallest number both denominators go into.

7. a | 1 | **30%**
b | 1 | **No. The graph just shows the percentage increase in sales, not the sales themselves. So Company B would have large increases but a much smaller number of sales.**
c | 1 | **No. The percentage increase in sales was less but it was still an increase in sales.**

8. a | 1 | **Width = y cm, Length = 2x cm**
b | 2 | The scale factor of the enlargement is new length ÷ old length = 2x ÷ y, or new width ÷ old width = y ÷ x, so $\dfrac{2x}{y} = \dfrac{y}{x}$.
(2 marks for correct explanation, otherwise 1 mark for referring to scale factor of enlargement or use of ratios.)
c | 1 | $y = \sqrt{2}x$ | Sophie is incorrect because she hasn't square rooted both sides of the equation correctly.
$\dfrac{2x}{y} = \dfrac{y}{x}$, so $y^2 = 2x^2$, so $y = \sqrt{2x^2} = \sqrt{2}x$

Answers

9.	a	1	**2 cm**	$4\pi = \pi r^2$, $r^2 = 4$ so $r = 2$ cm

9. a 1 **2 cm** $4\pi = \pi r^2$, $r^2 = 4$ so $r = 2$ cm

b 2 Hypotenuse is the diameter = 4 cm. Using Pythagoras, $\left(\sqrt{8}\right)^2 + AC^2 = 4^2$, so $AC^2 = 16 - 8 = 8$, so $AC = \sqrt{8}$.
AC = BC, so the triangle is isosceles. **(1 mark for using Pythagoras and 1 mark for showing AC = $\sqrt{8}$.)**

c 1 **4 cm²** ½ × base × height = ½ × $\sqrt{8}$ × $\sqrt{8}$ = 4 cm²

---

10. a 1 **1. modal age, 2. median age, 3. mean age**

b 1 **The mean is largest because it takes into account the ages of the adults, the others don't.**

TIP: You can see straight away that the modal age is 3. And the median must be either 3 or 4. A quick count up of the people gives 51 in total, so the median is 4.

---

11. a 1 **$\dfrac{1}{8}$** $\dfrac{3}{24} = \dfrac{1}{8}$

b 3 **Small** Probability of small tin being peaches is 3/10, probability of large tin being peaches is 4/14 = 2/7.
2/7 = 20/70, 3/10 = 21/70. So probability is higher with small tin.
(1 mark for saying "small", 1 mark for 3/10 and 2/7, and 1 mark for showing 3/10 is larger.)

---

12. a 2 Angle PTQ is y because triangle PTQ is isosceles, so angle PQT is $180° - 2y$. Angle PQT + x = $180°$,
so PQT = $180° - x$. So $180° - 2y = 180° - x$, $-2y = -x$, $x = 2y$.
(2 marks for correct explanation, otherwise 1 mark for getting angle PQT = $180° - 2y$ or $180° - x$.)

TIP: It's often a good idea to try and work out as many angles as you can. Then see what information you can use to answer the question.

b 2 **$y = 30°$** Angle TSQ = x as triangle TSQ is isosceles. Angle PTS = $90°$.
So using triangle PTS, $180° = 90° + y + x$, $180° = 90° + y + 2y$, $3y = 90°$, $y = 30°$.
(2 marks for correct answer, otherwise 1 mark for some correct working.)

TIP: Remember to use $x = 2y$ from part (a).

---

13. a 1 **£20** 200 ÷ 10 = 20

b 1 **£5** 2½% is 10% ÷ 4, 20 ÷ 4 = 5

c 2 **£269.50** 10% = 22, 2½% = 5.50, so 22½% = 22 + 22 + 5.5 = 49.50
Total price = 220 + 49.50 = £269.50
(2 marks for correct answer. otherwise 1 mark for finding 10% and 2½% correctly.)

---

14. a 1 **When x is even, $x(x + 3)$ is even**
b 1 **When x is odd, $x^2 + 1$ is even**
c 1 **$x^2 + x$ is always even.**

The simplest way to tackle questions like these is to pick an even or an odd number and substitute it into the equation.

---

15. 2 **2, 2, 3, 4, 9 or 2, 2, 3, 5, 8 or 2, 2, 3, 6, 7**
(2 marks for correct answer, otherwise 1 mark for 2, 2, 3 and two other numbers.)

TIP: You need to narrow down the options. The list has to begin 2, 2, 3,... and a mean of 4 means the five numbers have to sum to 20.

---

16. a 2 **57 cm²** ½ × (12 + 7) × 6 = ½ × 6 × 19 = 3 × 19 = 57 cm²
(2 marks for correct answer, otherwise 1 mark for some correct working.)

b 2 **684 cm³** Cross-sectional area × depth = 57 × 12 = 684 cm³.
(2 marks for correct answer, otherwise 1 mark for attempting to multiply area by depth. Award marks for correctly calculated answer using incorrect value from part (a).)

---

17. a 1 **Negative correlation**
b 2 **Intercept must be more than 20. Gradient must be negative. (1 mark for each correct reason.)**

---

18. a 1 **1547** 2.38 × 650 = 23.8 ÷ 10 × 6.5 × 100 = 154.7 × 10 = 1547

TIP: Make sure your answers are sensible. For example, to work out "2.38 × 650", think, "two and a bit times 650 is going to be one thousand and something".

b 1 **0.65** $\dfrac{154.7}{23.8} = 6.5$, so $\dfrac{154.7}{238} = \dfrac{6.5}{10} = 0.65$

c 1 **238** $\dfrac{154.7}{6.5} = 23.8$, so $\dfrac{15.47}{0.065} = 23.8 \times \dfrac{100}{10} = 238$

KS3 Maths Paper 3B Calculator Allowed

Q	Marks	Correct answer	The bit in the middle tells you how to get to the answer	Useful tips

1. a | 1 | **2**
b | 1 | **-10**
c | 1 | **8**

TIP: <u>Careful</u> with powers — in part (c) you only square the x, not the whole thing.

---

2. a | 2 | **BestXchange** — BetaTravel gives 82 ÷ 60 = 1.366... euros for £1, or 60 ÷ 82 = £0.731... for 1 euro. BestXchange gives 100 ÷ 72 = 1.388... euros for £1, or 72 ÷ 100 = £0.72 for 1 euro. So BestXchange is better value.
(1 mark for correct calculation of either rate and 1 mark for correct answer.)

b | 1 | **138.89 euros** — $\frac{100}{72} \times 100 = 138.89$ euros

---

3. a | 1 | **a = 65°** — PQR is an isosceles triangle, so a must be = 65°.
b | 1 | **b = 65°** — b is the alternate angle to a and so must be the same.
c | 1 | **c = 115°** — b + c = 180°, so c = 180° − 65° = 115°.
d | 1 | **d = 45°** — Angles in triangle RQS add to 180°, 180° − a = 115°, so d = 180° − 115° − 20° = 45°.

---

4. a | 1 | **n^2** — TIP: You need to recognise common sequences like square and cube numbers.
b | 1 | **$n^2 + 1$** — Each term is 1 more than the square numbers.
c | 1 | **$3n^2$** — Each term is three times the square numbers.
d | 1 | **$2n^2 + 1$** — You get each number by doubling the square numbers and adding 1.

---

5. | 2 |

(1 mark for the semicircle radius 6 cm and 1 mark for the quarter circle radius 2 cm. Or 1 mark overall if the right construction is attempted, but not drawn accurately.)

---

6. a | 1 | **6n + 3** — 2n + n + 5 + 3n − 2 = 6n + 3
b | 1 | **2n + 1** — Mean = total ÷ number of servings = (6n + 3) ÷ 3 = 2n + 1.
c | 2 | **10** — 2n + 1 = 11, so 2n = 10. **(2 marks for correct answer or 1 mark for using the correct method but getting the wrong answer.)**

---

7. | 3 | **$\frac{1}{4}$** — Probability of a head on 10p coin is $\frac{2}{3}$. Probability of all heads is $\frac{1}{2} \times \frac{1}{2} \times \frac{2}{3} = \frac{1}{6}$.

Probability of all tails is $\frac{1}{2} \times \frac{1}{2} \times \frac{1}{3} = \frac{1}{12}$. So probability of all the same is $\frac{1}{12} + \frac{1}{6} = \frac{3}{12} = \frac{1}{4}$.

(3 marks for correct answer, otherwise 1 mark for getting probability of head (or tail) on 10p coin and 1 mark for getting probabilities of all heads and all tails.)

---

8. | 2 | **72 kg** — New weight is $\frac{17}{16}$ of old weight. $\frac{1}{16}$ of old weight is 76.5 ÷ 17 = 4.5 kg. Old weight is 4.5 × 16 = 72 kg.

(2 marks for correct answer, otherwise 1 mark for attempting to divide by 17 and multiply by 16.)

---

9. | 2 |

Olivia is 6 months older than Bill — B − 0.5

Mateus is half Bill's age — B + 0.5

Ailsa is 6 months younger than Bill — B + 1

Chris is 1 year older than Bill — 0.5B

(1 mark for 1 expression joined correctly, 2 marks for all expressions joined correctly.)

Answers

| 10. a | 2 | **7x – 15** | $3x - 9 - 6 + 4x = 7x - 15$
(1 mark for correctly multiplying out without simplifying and 1 mark for simplification.) |
| b | 2 | **$2x^2 - 7x + 3$** | $2x^2 - x - 6x + 3 = 2x^2 - 7x + 3$
(1 mark for correctly multiplying out without simplifying and 1 mark for simplification.) |

| 11. | 2 | **134** | Billie eats $(4 \div 7) \times 70 = 40$, Anjum eats $(3 \div 5) \times 40 = 24$, Catie eats 70. $40 + 24 + 70 = 134$.
(2 marks for correct answer, otherwise 1 mark for calculating either Anjum or Billie's total.) |

12. a	1	**0.15 m**	
b	1	**0.00015 m²**	*TIP: Remember: 1 m = 1000 mm, so 1² m² = 1000² mm².*
c	1	**145 mm and 155 mm**	Lower bound = $150 - 5 = 145$ mm. Upper bound = $150 + 5 = 155$ mm.

13. a	1	**0 - 4**	The modal group is the one with the highest frequency.
b	3	**6.5 days**	Use the mid-interval values: $[(2 \times 14) + (7 \times 8) + (12 \times 5) + (17 \times 3)] \div 30 = 195 \div 30 = 6.5$ **(If you get the wrong answer; you can still get 1 mark for multiplying the mid-interval values by the frequencies, and 1 mark for dividing the total by 30.)**
c	1	**Because the mid-interval values are used I the calculation - not the exact values.** **(1 mark for similar comment)**	

| 14. a | 1 | **Anna earns £6 per hour, David earns £8 per hour.**
Anna marks 3 papers per hour, $3 \times 2 = £6$. David marks 4 papers per hour, $4 \times 2 = £8$. | |
| b | 3 | 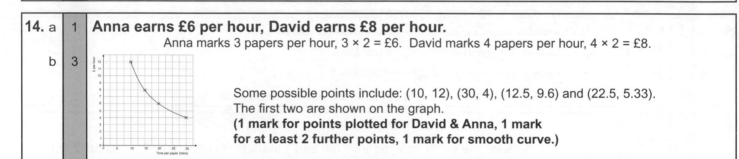 Some possible points include: (10, 12), (30, 4), (12.5, 9.6) and (22.5, 5.33).
The first two are shown on the graph.
(1 mark for points plotted for David & Anna, 1 mark for at least 2 further points, 1 mark for smooth curve.) | |

15. a	2	**Right** —	both of them get 20% of the questions right. **(1 mark for right and 1 mark for a suitable explanation.)**
b	2	**Wrong** —	sale price is 90% of original price. New price is 110% of sale price = 110% of 90% = 99%. So new price is not the same as original price. **(1 mark for wrong and 1 mark for a suitable explanation.)**
c	2	**Wrong** —	price in April is 120% of previous price. Price in May is 120% of price in April = 120% of 120% = 144%. That's a 44% rise in two months. **(1 mark for wrong and 1 mark for a suitable explanation.)**

| 16. a | 1 | **0.175** | Total no. of sixes = 42, total no. of throws = 240. Estimated probability = $42 \div 240 = 0.175$. |
| b | 1 | **No, as this is only a little above $\frac{1}{6}$ (0.167) and this is close enough to $\frac{1}{6}$ to suggest that the paper is wrong.** **(For 1 mark, must have comparison with 1/6.)** | |

| 17. a | 1 | **$\sqrt{3^2 + 8^2}$** | Using Pythagoras' theorem, $EF = \sqrt{DE^2 + DF^2} = \sqrt{3^2 + 8^2}$ |
| b | 2 | **3.85 m** | $BF = \sqrt{AF^2 - AB^2} = \sqrt{6^2 - 4.6^2} = \sqrt{36 - 21.16} = \sqrt{14.84} = 3.85$ **(to 3 significant figures)**
(1 mark only for correct working but wrong answer.) |

| 18. | 2 | E.g. Any two of: **r = 1, h = 36; r = 2, h = 9; r = 3, h = 4; r = 6, h = 1.** (1 mark for each correct set.) |

| 19. | 2 | **a = 2 cm, b = 4 cm** | Scale factor of enlargement = $AD \div AE = 15 \div 12 = 1.25$. $AC = AB \times 1.25 = 8 \times 1.25 = 10$, so a = 2 cm. $BE = CD \div 1.25 = 5 \div 1.25 = 4$, so b = 4 cm.
(1 mark for each correct value, otherwise 1 mark overall for some correct working.) |

MHB33